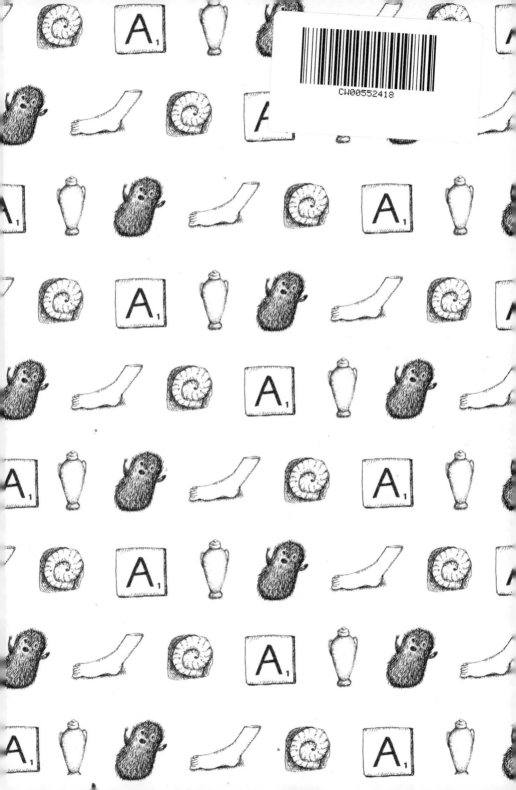

Sally—dear heart,
Something to lift above
your spirits ...
ceiling level
or cieling level.
very much love,

August 2013

Published in 2012 by Man in the Quote, Totnes, Devon

Design and layout by Frances Crow, following the format established by Jack Dean and Rob Steer of Silk Pearce in *The Hole in the Sum of My Parts* (Poetry Trust)
Printed and bound in the UK by TJ International, Padstow, Cornwall.

ISBN: 9-780957-4891-0-3

Also by Matt Harvey
The Hole in the Sum of My Parts (The Poetry Trust)
Where Earwigs Dare (Green Books)

And for kids
Shopping With Dad (Barefoot Books) illustrated by Miriam Latimer

Also illustrated by Claudia Schmid
Schabernak (Hammer) text by Margaret Klare

MAN
IN THE
QUOTE

MINDLESS BODY
SPINELESS MIND

MATT HARVEY

ILLUSTRATIONS BY
CLAUDIA SCHMID

for my family, near and far

CONTENTS

Strange Creatures Meeting

INTRODUCTION

This book is a miscellany, a motley mélange of stories and poems that have been gathering metaphorical dust in the imaginary drawers of spurious writing desks for some time. In making my selection I've tried to steer a path between self-indulgence and craven people-pleasing, and have thus included pieces frequently requested at performances alongside those people specifically ask me not to do.

Some of the poems have accompanying illustrations by Claudia Schmid, and some of Claudia's pictures are illustrated by poems. These are in the book-within-a-book, *Strange Creatures Meeting*. The first four poems in this section were inspired by Claudia's original drawings. I'm delighted to be working with Claudia and hope this book brings her work to a wider audience. I'm not saying though that you, the reader, are wide.

The book contains more prose than poetry but more poems than prose pieces, which sounds paradoxical but isn't. Three of the stories continue a tradition established in my previous books of misrepresenting the town of Totnes (twinned with Narnia) where I live. *Putting It Across* and *Regaining the Ashes* are noticeably more naturalistic than the other stories which, to a greater or lesser degree, invite a suspension of disbelief, a willingness to go-with, perhaps a gentle lowering of standards.

Also included are the continuing adventures of Empath Man as broadcast on BBC Radio 4, which of necessity include the opening scene that appeared in *Where Earwigs Dare*. Although talks re the film version broke down early – I suspect my email ended up in Warner Bros spam folder – I am optimistic that an all-star production of Empath Man the Musical will hit a stage near you soon.

I do hope you enjoy this book. I would, wouldn't I? And I do. I love books. They are at once a comfort and an escape, educational and potentially transforming. However for all its depth and insight, for all that it grapples with the very stuff of life, rest assured this book will leave your life the way it found it.

SAY IT WITH FLOWERS
A time-lapse love story

From his garden he could see her garden, as she his, from hers.
He realised she was the woman from the garden centre. She'd
smiled at him. He'd smiled back. He saw her hastily putting
down Pride & Prejudice when he came to buy his things. She'd
blushed.

He went back three days running, bought things he needed in
small batches, then things he didn't need in smaller batches.
"Thank you".

He earned 500 loyalty points, and they gave him a string bag of
bulbs. Which gave him an idea.

He chose a patch and planted them. YOUR BEAUTIFUL. No
apostrophe. No e. They didn't all come up.

YO   BE   IF

He wondered if she'd got the message. Or any message.
Probably not. Time passed.

Come spring, after the first snowdrops, there, in neat crocuses:
PARDON?

Surging with adrenalin he bought two bags of bulbs. All
the same this time. Fritillaries. Tenderly reiterated: U R
BEAUTIFUL.

There, he'd said it. The wait was difficult. Then they didn't really
synchronise. While some were still just peeking through the
soil the keen ones spelt: UTIFU. The rest would catch up soon.
Before they did though, strong winds in the night flattened the
UTI.

She woke to the message: F U

He panicked. He should have fluffed up the others, propped
them with sticks if necessary, instead he mowed them all down,
hoped she'd not seen.

Puzzled, but enjoying the botanical banter, she planted blue, yellow and red primula: F U 2.

He was crestfallen. Would not trust fritillaries ever again. Painstakingly he planted penitent red lupins. OOPS SORRY. Then across his former lawn with cornflowers, NO OFFENCE MEANT

Feeling for him, she replied in January, NONE TAKEN – in snowdrops planted compassionately but perhaps not as carefully as before. What he saw was I M TAKEN

A bitter blow. He knew what he had to do. Bravely he planted hardy pansies, let his house and rented a flat.

She was sorry to see him go, and surprised to read GOODBYE, GOOD LUCK.

Two years later he moved back. She spotted him, out tidying the garden the tenant had let slide.

Shyly she planted grape hyacinth. HI. He responded cautiously, in delphiniums, HI. She, in careful crocuses: R U OK?

He'd had enough. Speak and be damned. He blurted out, in unequivocal red tulips bought full-grown. I [HEART] U

She replied almost immediately, a smiley face in happy marigolds.

Marigolds. Marry-golds. Yes. He began to dig, his trench so deep she could read WILL YOU… She went indoors to sow seeds in a tray.

Before his bulbs came up she was knocking on his door, tea-tray in hands, her eyes inviting him to pull back the covering tea-towel. Revealed, in stenciled cress, the word, YES.

ALTERED STATES

The quest for mystical experience can take many forms. For some it's through contemplation – of the stars, of sacred geometry, of the navel – for some it's via meditation. Others prefer to ingest psychotropic substances. The word psychotropic suggests a hybrid musical form, a thrash-bossa nova, or a crazy blended fruit drink, but in fact it just means 'affecting mental states'.

What I'm about to tell you is as made-up as it is true.

A while ago now, friends and I and their dog, Moliere, went up onto Dartmoor – to look for magic mushrooms. We were looking respectfully, we thought. The plan was to trust the moor. If the moor wanted us to find magic mushrooms, well and good. If not, fair enough. Meanwhile we would help the moor by looking very, very hard.

Maybe we looked too hard. Maybe we were too fixed on what we wanted to find and the effect we wanted it to have on us. Because we were looking specifically to enter spiritual spaces. We wanted our psychotropic experience to be not just psychedelic – i.e. pertaining to a state of relaxation and pleasure, with heightened perception and increased mental powers generally – but mystical. We were looking, to paraphrase Blake, for the doors of perception to be made clean so we could see the world as it really is – infinite.

We sought the sweet synaesthesia of mingled senses, to see the music, taste the colours, smell the very shape of things, to paddle in the golden ocean of notions that washes on the shore of the humdrum. We wanted to know ourselves as a small essential part of a whole that is held and nourished by the unlikely umbilical of the universe, to teleport our imaginations to the surface of the planet Wonder and to set phasers to stunned.

We wanted to get *completely off our faces* – in a nice mystical way.

But it wasn't to be. We found no magic mushrooms. Instead we, or Moliere, found truffles – the underground edible fructification of the fungus of the genus Tuber – a delicacy in any culture. We'd asked the moors for a fungal gift and we'd been given one. Not the one we expected, but it would have been churlish to refuse, so we revised our plans based around the truffles.

We hadn't realised that nature favours complementary planting. Nature likes balance. Soft near hard. Dock leaves near nettles. It's almost as if nature has read a book about gardening. Antidote, poison. Effect, counter-effect. We had found the *yang* to magic mushrooms' *yin*. We had found tragic truffles. Yes. You may not have heard of them. That's part of the tragedy. For tragic truffles are, as we discovered, every bit as powerful as magic mushrooms, and longer-lasting.

Under their influence you experience the universe as expanding, every molecule moving inexorably away from every other molecule, and you know all intimacy is an illusion, all relationships merely security blankets woven of weeds doomed to biodegrade. And you experience yourself as an accidental confusion of reconstituted space debris pulled together blindly over blank millennia to create a semi-conscious being who knows its life to be a brief spasm of unfulfilled appetite sandwiched between infinite oblivions.

All of which added up to a real downer on our evening, because we had been planning to play charades.

THE BEST FORM OF DEFENCE

I've written before of the gentle market town in which I live, and if you've ever visited Totnes you'll surprised to hear that recently I was attacked. In broad daylight. On Totnes High Street.

Attacked!

Well, I say 'attacked.' It was one of those statue buskers. You know the ones – they dress in tin foil, crepe and silver paint and their movements are almost imperceptibly slow. So slow it can be difficult to discern what they're up to or where they're coming from. But he was looking at me with menace in his eyes, and I thought: I'm not taking any chances here. I'm going to defend myself.

I bent my knees, slipped fluidly into the Tai-Chi low-ceilinged room stance and began to skirt him, warily. The atmosphere was electric. Even so it was fifteen minutes before anyone realised there was a fight going on – but when they did they gathered round, chanting 'Fight! Fight! Fight!'

There's a real sense of community round here.

It was a close contest, the minimal subtlety of his movement against the mindful ebb and flow of my own. After forty-five minutes we still hadn't made any physical contact. We did, however, raise over thirty-seven quid, and we decided, spontaneously, to shake hands, split the money, and get on with what was left of the day.

Which brings me to the point of this story, which is that where I live it's not your body that's under threat, it's your *time*. It really is. You pop out in the morning for a pint of milk and newspaper, and you get home at dusk. Because you meet people. You ask how they are. And they tell you. In depth. And you listen, respectfully. And you in turn tell them of your hopes, dreams and symptoms. And so on. And on.

And that's why, although there are classes offered locally in
Tai-Chi, Tae Kwon Do, Karate, Judo and Aikido, I've signed up
for a brilliant new life-style specific self-defence class, called No
Kan Do™. It's a fusion of assertiveness training, martial arts and
modern dance. An all-terrain system of postures, movements
and phrases designed to guard your time against even the most
well-meaning adversary.

As with any martial art the dedicated student can progress
through the grades. To go up a belt in Karate a student must
hold their ground against a series of opponents of the grade
above. Similarly to attain your yellow belt in No Kan Do™
you have to keep the whole of Thursday afternoon free, while
established yellow belts try to get you to commit to events and
activities you don't really fancy. It's not easy. I failed my first
attempt, agreeing against my better judgement to look at the
etchings of a wistful man who I couldn't bear to disappoint.

My practice continues. I've moved up to an Intermediate class,
held weekly in a beautiful country house with high ceilings,
sloping lawns and its own library. Not that I've actually been
there. I'm beginning to get the hang of No Kan Do™.

TORQUAY BOYS

If you've noticed and been in any way intrigued by the waves made recently by my 'alternative' home town of Totnes you'll probably have heard about the cultural exchanges we've been doing with Torquay, up the road.

It started out pretty informally. I think they heard that we like our chanting in Totnes, so groups of Torquay residents – mainly young men aged between eighteen and thirty, mainly on a Friday or Saturday evening, after ten pm – began to come over and chant.

Their chanting is very different from ours. It goes: *TORQUAY BOYS, WE ARE HERE. SHAG YOUR WOMEN AND DRINK YOUR BEER!*

And to be honest, we Totnes men didn't really know how to respond. We felt left out, troubled. We tended to drift indoors, sit pensively, make a bit of salad. Then an enterprising men's group facilitator spotted a gap in the market. He began to run 'Holistic Hooliganism' workshops.

I thought: I should get along to that. I could learn something.

We stood in a circle to begin with and bonded over some swearing. It was bloody good. Then we did kicking each other to the floor – but wearing kung fu slippers, so it was just like a really intense Indian head massage.

Then he decided we were ready to do some chanting. After me, he said, and tried to lead us in *TOTNES BOYS, WE ARE HERE. SHAG YOUR WOMEN AND DRINK YOUR BEER!*

But we couldn't. We were ragged, we petered out. "What's the matter with you?" he said. One man murmured, "I'm actually off alcohol at the moment. I'm just drinking that fermented health drink, kombucha. So I couldn't really join in with integrity."

Another man was saying, "I don't like to go all the way with a woman on the first date. I need time to get to know her, to build up intimacy, I can't just, you know, jump right in. it's just not… me."

Our leader was very disappointed in us. He said, "You're rubbish." Washed his hands of us, walked away.

But a group of us, empowered by our low-key rebellion, our sticking up for own values, we made up our own chant. And we went to Torquay off our own bats – in the early afternoon I admit – and chanted our chant: *TOTNES MEN, WE ARE HERE. RESPECT YOUR WOMEN AND DRINK YOUR KOMBUCHA!*

And I like to think we were shown a bit of respect. People gave us room on the pavement. Some gave us low-denomination coins.

And now when the Torquay Boys come round to Totnes of an evening, we empowered men don't drift indoors and make salad. But we gather, some distance away, on the high ground (representing the moral high ground). Then we visualize healing white light all around them – and there's nothing they can do about it – and chant: *YOU'RE GOING HOME WITH YOUR CHAKRAS REALIGNED!*

So we win.

CLOUDBUSTING

Do you know about cloud-busting? It sounds nebulous, but a lot of people do it. Kate Bush wrote a song about it. Essentially it's dispersing puffy fluffy cloud through the power of thought, of the focused mind.

I know. I was skeptical too. Then the Met Office moved to Exeter. It was relocated Met Office personnel joining our shamanic ramblers group that woke me up to it. They don't call it cloud-busting, they call it intercessionary meteorology. They do it all the time.

With the South Hams Shamanic Ramblers we took it a stage further. We thought, if we can disperse a bit of cloud then we can gather cloud to us. If we can gather it we can begin to shape it. If we all focus.

You've maybe seen cloud pics on the internet. A terrier, a dragon's mouth, a dolphin eating a sandwich – these aren't just flukey coincidences, they're the work of cloud-sculptors. Using the sky as a 3D sketchbook.

It's ephemeral, but great fun. An outdoor parlour game. The South Hams Shamanic Ramblers and Cloud-Sculptors took it too far one time. We decided to recreate Rodin's 'The Kiss'.

A full complement gathered with Tate postcards of the great sculpture, accumulated a wealth of co-operative cumulus and shaped it into a magnificent facsimile of Rodin's famous work – whose blend of eroticism and idealism makes it one of the great images of sexual love. Then the wind changed.

We had over-reached ourselves. Our fabulous cloud-sculpture came down around us, soaking, freezing and disorientating everyone. There were no fatalities, but that evening the local news ran with reports of Dartmoor walkers getting lost in a heavy snog...

AFFIRMATIVE

I received a lovely letter recently from a reader of my books basically saying I'm doing a good job. I found this really affirming. So affirming in fact that I turned it into an affirmation – 'I do a good job' which I went on to develop: 'I do a good job, the job I do is good. I am good, so is my job, I do a good job, me, a job done by me is a job well done. Well done me, I've done a good job, again, bravo, I'm a great me, a good job too, I've done a good job of being a great me.'

By repeating and developing this affirmation I learned a lot about myself and the world around me. I learned that, while it's good to be positive, positive thoughts aren't always the most accurate and can lead to domestic conflict. I learnt many things, and I decided to explore the subject of affirmations further and report back.

I saw two paths open to me – I could read widely and deeply and speak with erudite people, or I could affirm inwardly to myself over and over, 'I know a lot about affirmations, me. I know loads I do.' In the end I chose the course that I felt led me closer to my own inner knowing and involved less travel.

Affirmations are a great tool, one of the best forms of customising and conditioning consciousness. The idea is to identify what or how you wish to be, tell yourself you are that already, and watch as you become it. Our subconscious mind is deeply suggestible, relying not on reason to form its beliefs and attitudes but rather on repetition, which is why many of us pick up self-limiting beliefs to begin with. We can't reason these beliefs away. The subconscious is more impressed by Lewis Carroll's 'what I tell you three times is true'.

The trick is to steep ourselves in an alternative belief, infuse our being with this new attitude with such tenacity and enthusiasm it becomes our reality. An infusion applied with enthusiasm is called an enthusion, and this is what makes the crucial difference. But you have to be careful and you have to be realistic. It's one thing affirming 'I'm a lithe, cheerful woman with a wonderful relationship,' but that won't work if, to start with, you're a squat, sullen man under a restraining order. Best then to keep it to something simple yet positive like 'I have nice teeth', or 'I shall be revenged'.

Another pitfall is clarity of language. If our conscious minds see the world 'through a glass, darkly', the subconscious hears 'through a well-lagged partition, hardly,' so when repeating an affirmation in your head, make sure you enunciate clearly. I once struggled in a cross country race because my affirmation 'my needs are met' had been heard within as 'my knees are wet' and I developed painful water on the knee. And many would-be mystics seeking to infuse themselves with humility have inadvertently induced a deep humidity, so not only do they become insufferably muggy but their followers go clammy and stick together.

It demonstrates the power of affirmations though.

It's worth remembering that affirmations are just one end of a continuum with denial at the other end. Many British people have trouble with affirmations that are too positive and prefer something from the denial end of the spectrum. Rather than 'I've done a good job' they're more comfortable saying, 'Hmmm, not bad', or 'Hey, it could be worse'. But again, I'd advise caution. Affirmations are like multivitamins where only about 20% is absorbed by the system. With 'Hey, it could be worse' that 20% might be 'Hey', or it might simply be 'worse'. Conditioning the subconscious is an inexact science.

You're better off with something non-specific on detail but positively positive. Something like: 'Lovely, splendid, well done everybody', or 'Wow, terrific, nice one!' or best of all, 'It's okay, thanks, I'm fine. '

APOSTROPHYPSE NOW

Here's some graffiti I saw in an arts centre the other day: 'God is in the detail's.' Some of you will have winced when you read this. Because God *is* in the details, but the god of details, and we who serve this god, are offended. By the unnecessary apostrophe, I mean.

Q: How do you cure an anal retentive of obsession with correct punctuation? A: Give them semi-colonic irrigation.

There, you see? I have a sense of humour about it. I can laugh at myself – or *up* myself, even, if you think about it. I'm not an extremist. I don't go round advocating capital punishment for those who abuse the apostrophe. Not unless they compound the offence by confusing 'complementary' with 'complimentary'.

Some people say that to use an apostrophe preposterously is no catastrophe and that punctuation muscles should be allowed to atrophy. I disagree. Nor do I go along with the 7th Day Punctuationalists for whom such mis-use is akin to blasphemy.

I'm somewhere in-between. I've broken rules in my time. I was there in the 70's when the punk movement challenged the restrictive grammatical practices of the day. Few people now remember – or admit – that 'punk' was short for punctuation, that the notorious safety pins were symbolic of the apostrophe – of all punctuation – roaming wild and free. This is what thrilled the young and made the establishment quake in their sensible shoes. Heady days.

But even Johnny Rotten grew up, changed his name and bought a Fowler's Modern English Usage. And it might well have been a former punk-turned 7th Day Punctuationalist who responded to the graffiti in my local café: 'T, is, 4, testical's' with, 'Testicle's what? What does the testicle have? Use the flower of the apostrophe wisely'. It is a sad and beautiful piece of responsive graffiti.

Let me offer a new phrase to all 7th Day Punctuationalists who feel tarred by the anal retentive epithet. We are not what they say we are. We are anally redemptive. We are the Defenders of God's Little Details. We are difficult to live with sometimes.

INEDIA
It's nutrition, Jim, but not as we know it

We live in an age of diets, eating disorders, obesity, size 00 models, detox programmes, fasts, fast foods and 'heroin chic'. An age when people turn to new, challenging, extreme diets as we attempt, desperately, to 'get healthy' once and for all.

There are more recognised dietary groups than ever before: Vegetarians, Lacto-Vegetarions, Galacto-Vegetarions, Pescetarians, Vegans and Fruitarians – who even Vegans find strict. These days the ultra-strict even have their own eating disorder, Orthorexia Nervosa – honestly, look it up – an obsession with food-purity so all-consuming it's tantamount to self-harm.

I shan't be covering any of these here. I'm going further out. I'm going to talk about 'Inedia'. Non-eating. The noun derived from Inedia is 'Inediate' – its pronunciation is somewhere between 'immediate', 'inebriate' and 'an idiot'. The best known kind of Inediates are called Breatharians. Breatharians are often described as living on light, or 'prana'. Some people hear 'prana' as 'piranha' and get them mixed up with pescatarians (aka cod-botherers) which is a mistake.

Breatharians divide into two camps: Deep and Shallow. Deep Breatharians take long, slow breaths and are meditative and relaxed. Shallow Breatharians by contrast take lots of short, quick breaths and, though less serene than their Deep counterparts, get more done in a day.

Breathing Disorders

Being Breatharian isn't necessarily any protection against the same problems that afflict those of us hooked on matter. Many matter-munchers in Winter suffer from Seasonal Affective Disorder (SAD). Similarly, a lack of light leads some Breatharians to suffer Disorientating Existential Affective Disorder (DEAD).

Some also develop breathing disorders: Binge-breathing, for example, leads to puffiness and hyperventilation. Afterwards the binge-breather may try to compensate by breathing out more than they breathe in, which in turn leads to them looking like they've been vacuum-packed.

Infotarians

A less well-known form of Inedia is Infotarianism – living off a diet of pure information. Infotarianism isn't a diet that you seek out, it finds you. They notice themselves drawn to certain texts, websites, broadcast media, and find themselves…strangely replete. In one man's case he spent three days grazing on Google without eating or drinking and when he logged off he found that he'd put on weight.

Infotarians have learnt the hard way that informing themselves about Infotarianism is analogous to cattle being fed ground bones of other cattle, a kind of correspondence cannibalism which induces the infotarian equivalent of mad cow disease.

For this reason it was impossible to have any of this checked for accuracy by an actual Infotarian, and you may choose to take it with a pinch of salt.

DO THE RIGHT THING

Where's a book of new age etiquette when you need it? Eh?

I'm posting a letter, mid-morning, outside the HSBC bank, when a woman I know says "Hello." "Hello," I say, right back. Why wouldn't I? It's only polite. "How're you doing?" she asks, "Fine'" I say, "and you?" "You look terrible," she says. "Oh, really?" I'm a little stunned by this, but I rally. "I feel all right." "Are you sure?" she asks, concerned, "you look *dreadful*." I think I smile. To be honest she doesn't look *that* great herself. "Really, I'm okay." "I mean," she speaks slowly for emphasis, "you look awful. Really rough." I don't know what to say to this. She adds, reflectively, "You don't look well." "I'm fine," I say, "underneath." She peers at me, unconvinced.

I can see she's not going to let me not be not okay. So I play the percentages. "I'm a bit tired, maybe." "You're tired?" "Rough night last night, kids woke up a few times, you know, probably makes me look… rough." "Ah, you're not sleeping well." "Not as well as I'd like. But, you know, I'm okay, just a bit tired." "You look really, really tired." "Well there you go, that's tiredness for you. It makes you look really tired." "And unwell." "Yes, it can look like that." Pause.

Well, I've given a bit, I've acknowledged a tiredness I'm not fully in touch with, so I make my leaving sounds. "Got to trot along. See you." My feet are doing okay with walking away when she says, "I'll send you a Reiki." I blink. I think, but don't say, "You're going to *send* me a *Reiki?*"

My brain automatically flicks through some options I could say, "No, please, that's not necessary," thus restarting the exchange. I could say, "Oh for God's sake, just leave me alone." Which would just prove that I wasn't fine all along. I could say, "Yes, you do that," in a tone of utter indifference or, "Yeah, whatever," which would be even worse. But I do none of these. At a loss, I say, "Thank you!" brightly, with what I hoped was a warm smile.

And I walked away feeling pretty chuffed with myself, till I thought, But what happens next time I see her? What do I say? If I say nothing I'm ungrateful or insensitive. If I say, "By the way did you ever send me that Reiki?" I'm questioning both the efficacy of Reiki healing, sent or otherwise, and the integrity of the person who'd said they'd send it. And if I say, "Hi, thanks for sending me the Reiki. Mmmm it was great, I feel a lot better now," I risk appearing both fraudulent and extremely sarcastic.

The whole thing is fraught. And where can I turn for assistance?

THWOK!

bounce bounce bounce bounce
thwackety wackety zingety ping
hittety backety pingety zang
wack thwok thwack pok
thwikety thwekity thwokity thwakity
cover the court with alarming alacrity
smackety dink, smackety dink
boshety bashity, crotchety crashety
up loops a lob with a teasing temerity
leaps in the air in defiance of gravity
puts it away with a savage severity
coupled with suavity
nice
15-love

bounce bounce bounce bounce
thwak thwok plak plok
come to the nettety
bit of a liberty
quickly regrettety
up goes a lobbity
hoppety skippety
awkwardly backwardly
slippety trippety
tumble & sprawl
audible gasps...
15-all

opponent asks how is he?
courtesy, nice to see
getting up gingerly
brushity thighsity
(all, if you're asking me
bit big-girls-blousity)

bounce bounce bounce
whack thwok plik plok
into the corner then straight down the linety
chasety downity, whackety backety
all on the runnity, crossety courtety
dropety vollety – quality, quality…

… oh I say what impossible gettery
no, umpirical rulery – nottety uppity –
oooh – doesn't look happety
back to the baseline
muttery muttery muttery muttery
30-15

bounce bounce bounce,
thwacketty OUT
2nd serve
bounce bounce bounce
thwacketty BLEEP
Let

bounce bounce bounce
thwacketty – slappity
thwackety – thumpity
dinkety-clinkety, gruntity-thumpity
clinkety
thump!
30-all
fistety pumpety, fistety pumpety
COME ON!

quiet please
bounce bounce bounce
thwacketty thwoketty
bashetty boshetty
clashety closhety
OUT!
what?
lookaty linety, lookaty line-judge
wearily query
umpire upholdery, indicate inchery
insult to injury
40-30
give line-judge scrutiny
face full of mutiny
back to the baseline
through gritted teethery
muttery mutiny mutiny muttery

bounce bounce bounce bounce
thwak thwok thwak plok
thwakety plik, thwoketty plak
to-ity fro-ity, fro-ity to-ity
slowity quickety, quickety slowity
turnety headety, headety turnity
seems like we've been here a bloomin eternity

leftety rightety. rightety leftety
topety spinnety, backhandy slicety
lookety watchety, scratchety bottity
fabulous forehand, backhandy slicety
furious forehand, savagely slicety
fearsome ferocity vicious velocity
bilious backhand blasted so blistery
half a mile out but that line judge is history
OOOWWWWWWWWT!

GAME
(new balls please)

MATTHEW AHMET, SHAOLIN MONK

it's nice to see you in repose
unflustered in your mustard robes
a peaceful smile upon your face
and when you move, you move with grace
but Matthew, think about the waste...

you could have done texting, had big macs and fries
you could have had facebook and ipods, told lies
on your CV, had piercings, done beer things
with peer-pressured mates

but you wanted to go and to live in Henan,
learn to leap, and be still, and to speak Mandarin
and to harness your Qi, wear the robes of Shaolin

you could have had dvds, downloaded mp3s, ringtones
are you listening to me? You missed *so much TV*

Matthew Ahmet, dammit, you could have been a consumer

but you wanted to move like an eagle, a cat,
to be strong from within, and to speak Mandarin

you could have had rap, hip-hop, garage and indy bands
death metal disco thrash, ambient trance
but you wanted to learn discipline and to dance
and to coach, and to teach, and reach out to the young,
who may listen to you when they learn what you've done
and think: *What could I become?*

because you gave it all up for the key to your Qi
to follow your star till it wasn't a star
just the thing that you do and the way that you are
for you have discipline, and you speak Mandarin
and you follow the way of Shaolin

BUS POEM: ON AND OFF

Just us in the queue
so we got on together,
the bus being busy
sat next to each other
It stopped at my stop
but I didn't get off
When seats became free
she still sat next to me
Till there was just us
on the top of the bus
And we finally got off
with each other

RUDOLF NUREYEV'S BALLET SHOE

this ballet shoe that bore his weight
now bears his signature, a date
now holds his memory and his shape

this is the ballet shoe that knows
the flexing of Nureyev's toes
the shoe that he stepped in and leapt landing lightly
that stood strong en demi-pointe trembling slightly

nightly
most likely

how could such a shoe forget
the knowledge absorbed with his sweat
the memory of each pirouette
of grand battement a la seconde
that's danced en demi ronde de jambe
with attitude and with aplomb

he'd hoist a ballerina skyward
making human form ethereal
as if she were made of plywood
or some other light material

who could not but be inspired
by this ballet shoe so long retired
even this shoe so long asleep
may hold within it last leap

who wouldn't step out from their desk
and try for one last arabesque
to leap, to fly, to hit the deck
to sit and write this poem
with a really sore neck

BUS POEM: BUSKER

when the busker at the bus stop
did an uninvited guest spot
the people in the bus queue
were looking pretty desperate

when the bus came
to their rescue
there were none left
in the bus queue
for the busker to play for
so he got on the bus too
and did an encore

THEORETICAL PHYSICISTS (PROBABLY)

they're celebrants of elegance
apologists for awesomeness
give physical reality excruciating scrutiny
each and every moment is a photon opportunity

they breathe rarified air on the cusp of the known
where anti-particular unseeds are unsown

in the face of this immensity
my mind feels it has the density
of a shortish sort of Planck
it feels this constantly
(and with a silent c)

let me explain…
if the energy (E) of a particle (P)
and its dignity (D) are all relative (R)
to the way they are seen (S)
or misunderstood (Mmm)
it's my best guess (BG)
that they're subject (SJ)
to the forces (FC)
of ignorance (I)
the desire to sound deep (Duh)
of emotional baggage (Ebb)
floaty otherness (Flow)
and are tempered (ey up)
by the deep knowing (Kuh!)
that we find in our heart (Huh!)

so that far from chanting a secular Om Shanti with the cognoscenti
we wind up sipping skinny latte with the ignorati

all of which is best expressed by the equation:
E over P subdivided by D and surrounded by R
equals 2 pi r spurned magnified by Kuh! Huh!
undermined by I O and undeterred by Oo-er

which is why the light reaching us from Andromeda
is never truly fresh
and inertia has momentum
of its own

BUS POEM: SKYGLOW

because of skyglow
from the bright
street lights
we don't see the stars
from the city
at night
though once quite late
we saw a bright
white arse
moon from the top deck
of the one nine eight

TILLY AND CLIFF

*(Tilly and Cliff are two life-size figures made by sculptor Lal Hitchcock
entirely from flotsam and jetsam. This is their song.)*

You're made out of odds and I'm made out of ends
We're cast-off bits and bobs but we're more than just friends
We have so much in common, we both know how very odd it is
To be composed of off-cuts & extraneous commodities

Your various parts all add up to a wonderful sum
They're all fit for purpose, just not their original one
You're more than the sum of your parts. You know what a man wants.
You stepped out of the sea like a Bond-girl. But not all at once.
   You're the woman I want. *You're the man I adore*
   I'm so glad you washed up on my shore

You're quite simply one of my favourite people
An incremental immigrant – not an illegal
We can still share a thermos, and magical moments
If you don't mind the age-gap between my components
   If there's doubt in your mind then let me reassure:
   I'm so glad you washed up on my shore

I like your beach-comb-backed hair and your broom brush bristles
When I kiss you it's like being tickled with thistles
I like your fishnet fullness and your frontal bumps' protuberance
Although they're made of plastic they've a natural exuberance
   When you come in to view I can't help but go 'phwoar!'
   I'm so glad you washed up in my shore

You're my Mr Right – you're my Ms Even Righter
My High Tide high five you're my love-at-first-sighter
You're more, I adore you, you're my Mr Rightest

You're made of debris and I'm made of detritus
Our parts may wear out but our love will endure
I'm so glad you washed up on my shore

    Let's not be afraid of the facts, turn and face them
    If bits should drop off we can always replace them
    If the blues come along we'll just turn and chase them
    Away…

Though tenderly assembled we are neither of us cosseted
We've been buffeted and bashed about and bashed about and buffeted
I'm sorry for your troubles but I'm glad you were deposited
Along the same high tide line and your attitude is positive

You're winningly winsome. *You're handsome and then some.*
Are there finer men out there? Cos I've never met them
You can keep your fine fellows from Topsham and Epsom
I prefer my men from flotsam and jetsam
    You've the coastal charisma that I can't ignore
    I'll say it again as I've said it before
    At the risk of appearing a terrible bore
    I'm so glad you washed up on my shore

DEEP TIME

the moon looked down
    nothing much happened
the moon looked down
    still nothing
the moon looked at its watch
sighed
closed its eyes & decided to play a game
opening its eyes every million sun-spins

this was more like it

the moon saw time lapse topography
saw fins and ferns, splash and swish, scuttle, scurry
the unrelenting elements
the rugged old reliables
the prototypes of predators
of evolution's editors
incessantly impacting, interceding, undermining,
over-riding, interacting
always pressing, pressing, pressing
scorching, torching, frying, drying
screeching, wiping...

crustaceans crushed beneath oceans
the all-in-one indifferent ocean
cruising, crashing, lapping, lashing
bruising, bashing and caressing
saw the eros in erosion
the deep coma in commotion

the moon liked this game

single-selved creatures cropped up
shape-shifted and competed
were upgraded or deleted

hushed, then crushed
hushed, then crushed

the earth was at an impressionable age

strange shapes were pressed
into the confiding coast
this battered scattered scrapbook
weather-bound boxed set
of encrypted scripts
uncaptioned curiosities
crystallized catastrophes
where perishables met preservatives
crime scenes
past statutes of limitation
pre-sentience reports
enigmatic trinkets left in safe-deposit strata
items of sedimentary value
bones, husks, shells
small selves, small selves

and the paw-printed patio of the fossil pavement
ammonite avenue,
prehistoric contact sheet
scrawled with spirals
like children practising their autograph

a stone-cast of creatures that once came a cropper

archive, hard-drive, posterity press
vanity published pop-up book,

unreadable – until, so recently – a creature turned up
with opposable thumbs and disposable ethics
raisable eyebrows and a droppable jaw
a fine upstooping primate stood up to be counted
– homo erectus, o lord god protect us –
who became the sapient ape
that knows it's homo brevitus
who found the leisure-time to wonder
at these conundra in the tundra
these intriguers these enigmas
that left stretch-marks on our imagination
teased the three-tiered brain

and began to play join-the-bones
reanimate the ammonite
to infer the brontosaurus' breath
to see a snowflake melting on a diplodocus' tongue
the fossil of a pterodactyl's shadow
a short-armed tyrannosaurus' heavy tread,
to see it stamping
tamping tamping tamping

earth's offspring are amazed to discover
that before they were born
their mother
had a life of her own

when the moon next opens its eyes
it'll get a surprise

STRANGE CREATURES MEETING
illustrations by Claudia Schmid

THE BABY AND THE LADY

in a place that's nice and shady
there's a lovely little baby
crying sadly, crying gaily
and a kindly kneeling lady
feeding butter to the baby

but the baby's very hairy
is it clever of the lady
to be feeding baby dairy
should the baby be more wary
of the butter and the lady?

is it right and is it proper
to be feeding baby butter?
nobody is there to stop her
nobody is there to mutter
hey, go easy on the butter

maybe that's why baby's hairy
and it's hair's so thick and curly
maybe that's why baby's burly

'save me' cries the hairy baby
'have some butter' says the lady

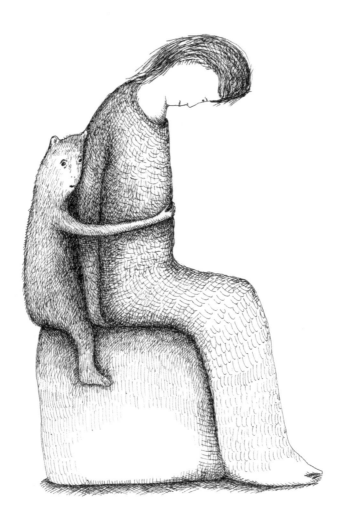

THE MONKEY ON MY BACK

I turn to him. He's here for me.
And in my time of misery
clings on to me, as I to him.
My sweet crutch, my prosthetic limb.

He doesn't say, Cheer up, chin chin,
or speak to me of shame or sin
as others do. Well-meaning, they
observe the way we're bound and say

in disapproval and alarm,
He'll bring you down he'll do you harm.
Beware the creature on your back,
his warm embrace is an attack.

Thank you, I say, for the advice,
although it isn't very nice.
But from the shadow where I sit
I must with due respect submit

it seems to me – I won't pretend –
the monkey on my back's my only friend.

THE SNUGS

fuzzynuzzled, mollycuddled
each in earthy warmth ensnuggled

held but not by way of capture
they put the gift-wrap into rapture

snug, not smug, but fully woolly
she's the axle of his pulley

he's the P on her pyjamas
they've drunk tea with Eastern lamas

conscious of themselves as creatures
neither actually encroaches

surfaces that share a boundary
shape that's cast in passion's foundry

and the spirals they define
have a humble, human line

swingers, but without a car-key
mathematic, Fibonacci

inlets to each others' angles
more than quantumly entangled

warm embrace of ambient ardour
the vessel in each other's harbour

eye to nostril, cheek to forehead
draped across each other's foredeck

arms around each other's acres
comfortable as baked potatoes

how come they're such a perfect fit?
trust me, they had to work at it

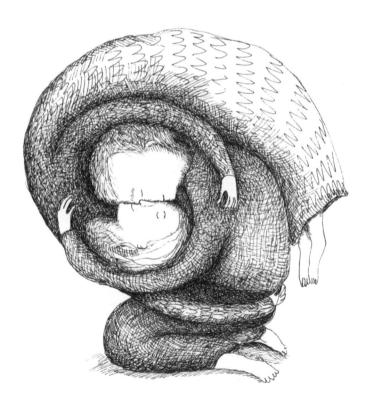

THIS FOOT

There's nothing intrinsically wrong with this foot.
In cases like this we examine the boot
and the socks and the trousers to get to the root.
Ask difficult questions that sometimes, I fear,
while easy to say, aren't so easy to hear.

Your interests, the foot's – are they one and the same?
Is it equally keen to be joined on to you?
I can't help but see things from the foot's point of view.
I'm a doctor. I'm trained.

It's nobody's fault if a foot doesn't fit.
A man and his foot are not joined at the hip.

I have taken a thorough, professional look
and I'll put it as strongly as it can be put:
There is nothing *intrinsically* wrong with this foot.

AMATEUR ASTRONOMERS

and some are called to watch the stars
to stay up late and scan the skies
on moonless nights with fleece and flask
to train self-educated eyes
with night-adjusted irises

they know what an aurora is
and how to plot each bright dot's orbit
participate in heaven's audit

perched on tripods pointing skyward
super strength zoom lenses lend
affordable home-hubble views
and they peruse
Io, Ganymede, the Jovian moons

the rings of Saturn ,Venus' phases
they rest techno-augmented gazes
on their distant perfect curves

austere voyeurs

while here on earth
the pinpoint pricks of light observed
are living rooms with flickering screens

sat soft and vaguely comatose
before the soaps and talent shows
settee-bound households who reserve

the accolade of oohs and ahs
for different kinds of flickering stars
and viewing opportunities

a quiet step away from these
in voluntary darkness
with the patience of the ancients
in their small suburban fastness

anonymous astronomers
keep vigil with the vastness
and gaze through see-through skies
at free view stars

TWO LOVELY BLACK EYES

everybody loves a panda
quick to nibble, slow to anger
we feel tender toward the polar
brown bear, grizzly and koala
but we're fonder of the panda
can't but want to take a gander
at the one tonne two-tone bundle

deployed over the centuries
in overseas diplomacy

there's a made-up Chinese proverb:
after diplomatic blunder
you can always send a panda
international befriender
ace bridge builder and fence mender
you can depend upon a panda

the mammal that's based on a toy

to cap it all they can be coy
attempts to mate Chi Chi with An An
were, with hindsight, bound to founder
Chi Chi had her own agenda
wham bam? no thank you An An
bamboo? that'll do!
as love lives go, theirs was so so

Chi Chi's remains are still around though
visit, if you want to see 'em
the natural history museum

where the label really should say
what the label never would say:

Chi Chi. There's no panda finer.
Stuffed in Britain. Made in China.

THE HIDEOUS BLOAT

it appeared overnight, unannounced and unplanned
by the dubious grace of some sinister hand

from an ugly bump on the edge of the town
it grew into a hump, and then into a mound

its surface was slimy and quite sparsely grassed
it was tiny at first then increasingly vast

it was given its name by a popular vote
and they called it the Hideous Bloat

and it grew, and it grew
and nobody knew what to do

they could see no solution, find no antidote
to the growth of the Hideous Bloat

the Planning Committee received a petition
demanding that they refuse planning permission

before they could act the Bloat sprung a surprise
and blearily opened two big bloodshot eyes

"it has eyes, it's alive, it has eyes!" they all said
"it has eyes in what we now suppose is its head!"

a dozen feet downhill, travelling south
they discovered a nose, and a mean-looking mouth

that yawned a foul yawn, then sullenly spoke
"Get out of my face", croaked the Hideous Bloat

"Sorry!" they squeaked as they backed down the hill
all looking and sounding quite desperately ill

all looking in danger of imminent death
for the Hideous Bloat had shocking bad breath

and it grew, and it grew
and nobody knew what to do

it was Hideous, Bloated, and not at all pretty
so they called in an expert who drove from the city

she said, "There's no knowing, and therefore no telling
when the Hideous Bloat's going to stop its strange swelling"

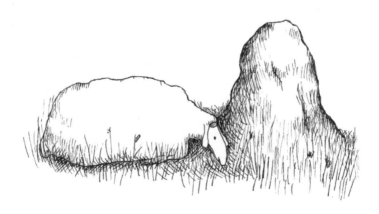

"but," she said, "the Law's clear, 'Topographical features
with eyes, nose and mouth shall be counted as creatures'"

and the townsfolk agreed she had spoken such sense
it was well worth the frankly enormous expense

then the Council debated and issued an edict
"the Bloat is alive," said the Mayor, "we must feed it!

for though we may find it obscene, unhygienic
revolting, repulsive and not very scenic

though we privately think it a source of infection
it's our civic duty to show it affection

we'll feed up the Bloat, that's a cast-iron promise"
and he winked at the Head of the Chamber of Commerce

and it grew, and it grew
and nobody knew what to do...

they fed it with leftovers, off cuts and scraps
fed it fat fetid burgers in musty old baps

fed it junk that they wouldn't accept at the dump,
sharp broken bottles and oil from the sump

one afternoon after guzzling a drink
with the flavour of drains and the fragrance of stink

the Bloat licked its lips with a leathery tongue
and wheezily whispered, "That's it. Nearly done."

it hissed out these words like a poisonous curse
took a deep breath, closed its eyes, and then... burst

with a pustulent pestilent bilious boom
it burst like a noxiously toxic balloon

and the gunk it sent up turned around and came down
in rank parcels of yuk on the sleepy old town

like a fountain of blackheads, a volcano of vomit
that massed overhead and then rained down upon it

and wherever the Hideous chunky hunks fell
the ground underneath slowly started to swell

to swell and expand, to expand and to grow
and the Planning Committee, as one, went, "Oh no!"

as a thousand foul Bloatlets of varying size
bulged ever upward and opened their eyes

and opened their Hideous mouth parts to gloat
the Bloat is dead – long live the Bloat!

and they grew and they grew
and nobody knew what to do

they could see no solutions, find no antidote
to the growth of the odious, wholly malodorous
repulsive, repellent, distinctly unpleasant
revolting, repugnant, misshapen, malignant
abhorrent, insanitary, ghastly, invidious
Hideous, Hideous Bloat

SNIFF AND TELL

If it was me, I think I'd want to know.
Time was, some faceless git in Personnel
could send a 3-word memo: – *WASH OR GO* –
Point made. Pain caused. Tough shit. That's life. You smell.

There ought to be a new word: *ethiquette* –
the fine art of compassionate plain-speaking.
It's so easy to say things you regret,
blurt hurtful words like minging, niff, rank, reeking…

…which conjure other words. Say, 'bullying'
then 'constructive dismissal' come to mind.
But how can we tell what's the cruel thing
and what is necessary, even kind?

Some people have a knack, a gift, a sense –
quite like horse-whispering (it's also known
as, quote, *Emotional Intelligence*) –
pick right time, good place, right words, pitch and tone.

For those of us with low scores in EQ
this verse will help to minimise distress;
point out pitfalls; advise on what to do.
That's why it's been cut out. Placed on your desk.

IDLE

for some people *idle's*
an unwelcome label
amounting to libel
they'll bridle, get upset
for them *idler's* an epithet

they see
lounging scroungers, scheming spongers
loafers lapping up free lunches

what really needles re the idle
is not only do they have more fun
it's frankly amazing how much they get done

for the idle are quirky and perky and pert
& should not be confused with the merely inert

they're statistically more likely
to play the ukelele
and to take part in a ceilidh

to make time for sketching, hop-scotching, bird watching,
for stretching, plot-hatching, back-scratching,
and keeping in touch via actual touching

time for more than mere louche lazing
time for intellectual grazing
and, dare I say it, navel gazing

because the unexamined navel is not worth piercing

some say they daren't be idle
it's a question of survival
for the hand that rocks the cradle
to be idle's suicidal

a catastrophe of creditors
will circle us like predators
while we're reading Herodotus
and cultivating questionable philosophic qualities

but it's always worth checking
one's deep default setting

for while the icons on the desktop
say 'liberal' or 'libertarian'
maybe something on the motherboard's
still set to 'Presbyterian'

so go on, be idle, you deserve it
in fact, Idlers, rise up from your divan, futon, bean bag or sofa
and…

      …nah, sit down again, it isn't worth it

THE FROZEN FEW
A personal perspective on Cryogenics

say No to biodegrading and to corporeal corruption
death is not an absolute – just an interruption

while some await the last trumpet to sound to be saved
others wait for the *ping!* of a benign microwave

then they'll quench their curiosity
get futuristic tlc
their body fine-tuned by a Dr McCoy
their psyche seen-to by a Counsellor Troy

and while I wouldn't criticise
those few who would revitalise –
reconstitute – reanimate –
drop off without a wake-by date

to lie in liquid nitrogen
in a vacuum flask in Michigan
at minus 196 degrees
 – indefinitely –
doesn't do it for me

frankly it gives me the Martin Chivers

so – while there are those to whom, we know,
being ultra-deep-frozen gives a nice warm glow

rather than be a Birdseye sleeping beauty
woken with a techno-kiss
I prefer to achieve immortality
through unforgettable poetry

like this

RESPECTFULLY YOURS

Dear Sir, Dear Madam, To whom it may concern,
We write respectfully to reaffirm
our long-standing claim
to be seen of the flame.
There's not a woman or a man
we're better than or lesser than,
lesser than or better than, better than or lesser than.

We hope not to offend, nor to go on too long.
We sing partly to hear our own voice raised in song.
And to claim
we are of the same flame.

Who are we? We are those
to whom the world has been disposed
from time to time, from place to place
to show a disrespectful face.
And we are those who went before,
who knocked politely on the door,
and less politely on the wall.
Who called, but no-one heard their call.
Or their claim
to be of the same flame.

Those who've been hushed, who've been brushed to one side
who've been disregarded, derided, denied.
Those who've been called names,
we all know the names,
who've seen civilised people behave
in uncivilised ways.
Those who first made the claim
to be touched by the torch,

to be scorched by the flame,
and who'll come back again
and again to maintain
we are of the same flame.

We respectfully ask that you answer our call
for the dreams that we dream are not shallow or small
as we claim
to be of the same flame.

If you don't see the spark in us
but only see the dark in us,
there's one course we may yet pursue,
to always see the spark in you.
And though it may be slow in you,
and not something you know in you,
we will still see that glow in you
that sparks in every part of us
that's at the core and heart of us.
For all of us are Spartacus,
and we can all claim
to be of the same flame.

This flame is for everyone, no-one's exempt.
We're now held in esteem, who were held in contempt.
As we relish and cherish the worldly rewards
we accept the acclaim, we adore the applause,
but forgive us for keeping an eye on the door.
We've won a few scraps but we've not won the war.
The battles fought we do not regret.
We seek to forgive, we'd be fools to forget.

And we stand by our claim
to be of the same flame.

Thank you for your time
and for hearing our claim,
and for opening doors and of course
we remain,
respectfully yours

EMPATH MAN

(The contemporary Superhero with advanced listening skills and the ability to stay open and vulnerable in a tight situation.)

Episode 1: The Optiagra Effect

Compassionately foiling muggers and armed robbers is all in a day's walk for the Skinless Wonder.

Warehouse. Interior. Two desperate men, stuffing wads of cash into a duffel bag, look up, startled, as a man strolls casually through the double doors…

"Hi guys, looks like fun. Guess you must need the money pretty bad. Hey – I've been there. I know where you're coming from."

"Oh no, it's Empath Man! Don't let him disarm you with his self-deprecating charm and non-judgemental acceptance of who you are."

"I guess you must have felt quite an emptiness inside to need to fill it with bundles of cash. It's as if that duffel bag is your crumpled, deprived heart and this is an honest but confused attempt to meet its needs. I respect that. I find it moving."

"Damn you Empath Man. I don't want to talk about this shit right now."

"Don't let him get to you. Shoot him if you have to. "

"Hey, if you need to shoot me, I guess you need to shoot me. I feel very open and accepting of who you are and what you do."

"Shoot him!"

"I can't"

"Can't or won't?"

"I dunno, part of me wants to shoot him, another part just

wants to relax and hang out with the guy. The mixture of serenity and sheer ordinariness is strangely compelling…"

"OK. Give me the gun. I'll shoot him myself"

"Hey," Empath Man shrugs. "Whatever you need to do, you know, that's okay. Trust yourself. Who else can you trust? Who else have you ever been able to trust?"

"Goddamn it, I'm filling up!"

"What's he doing to you, Rodney, what's happening?"

"I don't know. It's this talk of trust. It's bringing up long-buried feelings."

"Long-buried what?"

"Feelings"

"Goddamn. You've got to fight it"

"I'm trying, it's just…they've been buried so long beneath encrusted layers of anger and cynicism, wrapped around in bravado and self-medication, it's kind of a big thing for me"

The soft man keeps talking. "What feeling are coming up? It's just me and your partner in crime here. You can tell us."

"Feelings of hurt, sadness, loss, betrayal, and, Oh God, no…."

"What is it? We both want to hear it…."

"A kind of self-loathing, a sense of shame, allied with a yearning of almost spiritual intensity"

"No, please, don't go spiritually intense on me now. I'm feeling pretty shaky as it is. Don't ….Oh God, it's the Police…"

Screech of tyres, slam of doors, pounding of meaty feet. It's Karma in a uniform. Empath Man keeps eye contact with the over-wrought robber as he greets the men in blue.

"Hello Officers, these two miscreants here were just opening up to some feelings about crime and the causes of crime, I'm sure they'll be more than willing to carry on down at the station."

The two are roughly cuffed and led away. "Come on then, miscreants, and stop snivelling, or we'll really give you something to cry about down at the cells."

"Hmmm. We all feel the desire to brutally punish others in order to bolster our own diminished sense of personal power."

"That's enough, Empath Man. I've got to hand it to you, another job well done. But I don't like your methods. They're effective, but they're sick"

"I understand, Officer, what it is to be both disgusted and threatened by emotional intensity and authentic intimacy. I too have insecurities gnawing at me like ravenous rats devouring the living tissue of self-worth. But thanks for the feedback. I'll take it on board - even though it may corrode my soul like the acid of early rejection by a parent or carer. But hey, I'm sensing you'd know about that...."

The officer turns away. Are those tears welling up? Probably.

Just another typical scene in the life of an atypical superhero. The Skinless Wonder. Empath Man. More raw feeling brought to the fore, over-articulated. More criminals brought to justice, such as it is. More law enforcement officers rubbed up the wrong way. You can't please everyone all the time. If ever. But hey, you've got to try. There are wrongs to be righted, and rights to be... whatever, validated... and a man's got to, you know, um, be, what a man happens to be... Hasn't he?

As usual, Empath Man is left alone to reflect. He wasn't always Empath Man. Used to be an ordinary guy. In middle management. Pulled his weight. No further than he had to, but he pulled it. Turned up, did his bit. Had a wife, Stella. Didn't deserve her. Sees that now. Stella wanted more. Said so. "I want us to see a Relate counsellor," "We don't need that," he said. "I do," she said. "We don't," he said. She said, "I feel taken for granted." He said, "Come here. Give us a kiss." Tch!

So what happened? Drugs. He took part in a drugs trial
that went horribly wrong. It was an anti-pessimism drug,
Optiagra. For middle-aged men who find it difficult to get their
hopes up. The change can be traced to that time. A friend at
EctoGriffTwine tipped him the wink. "Money for rope. Take a
happy pill. Tell a guy with a clipboard how you feel. Don't worry,
it's multiple choice. They have emoticons, you just point."

Strange how multiple choice questions, soft questions, led on to
harder questions. Open questions. How do I really feel? How do
you feel? Really? And then the knowing came. The emotional
antennae. Knowing, really knowing, how other people felt. He
didn't know how. And the emotional gravity. Feelings impelled
towards him. Why did people feel so deeply in his presence?
Why and how did they articulate so lucidly, express themselves so
urgently, passionately, helplessly? He couldn't say, but it was so.

Stella was like the cat who got the cream. Then became lactose
intolerant on the same day. Who could live with such a man? In
whose presence all feeling is amplified. Who knows how you
feel before you do. Who brings out the best in you at the worst
possible time.

So here he is. The Lone Listener. The man who puts the vigil
back in vigilante. Muttering to himself as he slopes home…

"I can't help wondering about the hand that fate has dealt me.
On the one hand it seems a good hand, with a lot of trumps in
it, or aces, which is good if you're playing whist… but what if
fate is playing poker, and there are no trumps? Sometimes I feel
so alone, other times I don't. What's all that about? Now I've
lost the thread of my monologue again. I keep doing this. I lose
focus so easily since I've been in touch with my feeling side…"

Nevertheless he notices the footsteps behind, picks up on the
malign intent of the two twenty-something nylon-clad white
boys, Alan and Stewart. But he doesn't mind. He's glad of the
company.

"Oi, mister. Mister Mutterer!"

"Me?"

"Yeah, you! Don't see anyone else muttering to themselves"

"It's something I do when I'm alone…"

"Well, since you're out here on your own, we'll have your money and your phone."

"What?" "What?" Stewart and Empath Man raise their eyebrows.

"You heard, Mister Mutter the utter nutter. You heard. You heard my word. Oi, stop laughing. You can laugh and you can splutter all the way down to the gutter, Mister Utter-Nutter Mutter"

"Sorry, I love the way you rhyme things like that, it's great."

"Yeah, well, I'm glad you think it's funny, now we'll have your phone and money…"

"What's with the rhyming, Alan?" "Don't really know. Just going with the flow."

"I'm afraid I don't carry money. Not for long. You're welcome to my phone"

Stewart takes it, sighs. "To be honest with you – and I'm armed with a knife so I'm not going to pussyfoot around your feelings – you should pay us to take this phone…"

"Sorry. That's no reflection on your abilities as a spontaneous poet or your charisma as an articulate and assertive individual. I think you're both great people. It's nice to meet you."

His sincerity's so transparent, Alan's caught off guard, "My monetary need's not been gratified, but my need for approval has been satisfied"

Stewart keeps focus. "Got any plastic?"

"I prefer natural fibres, cotton, wool…"

"I meant debit or credit cards…"

"Sorry. I've got a debit card. If that's any use."

"Any *use?* Do you have a decent balance in your account…?"

"Um, no. Stella cleaned it out."

"…a significant overdraft facility?" Empath Man winces and shakes his head apologetically.

"Well then…"

Even Alan's disappointed. "Just my messed-up luck to get stuck with a late-night lame duck"

Empath Man shares their disappointment. "It's such a shame we live in a society that sets less store by the emotional and artistic than the monetary. There are other currencies in which I'd like to think I had something to offer you."

Alan's intrigued. "Say what you mean, mean what you say, and get on with it, we haven't got all day."

Stewart's increasingly irritated "Actually Alan, it's night time."

"OK Stewart, Sorry for the breach, when it comes to it, it's just a figure of speech."

"Why you talking in rhyme Alan? It's freaking me out."

"I don't know why I talk this way, but it's okay, it's my newfound style, sets me apart from the rank and file. Apart from all this rhyming tomfoolery, I've noticed you've got a wider vocabulary. I think this guy's got something to do with it…"

"Yeah well can we just stab him and get on with our evening?"

"I wanted to once but now I can't go through with it…
Stabbing's not a thing to which I can relate, I'm so full of rhyme, I've not much room for hate"

"Great. It's all right for you, Alan, you've got a creative outlet. My mind's still full of frustration, a relentless jarring sense of thwarted possibility…"

"Well, Stewart, if I can call you that. You're a very different person. Very much your own man."

"Yeah you belong to yourself, you're nobody's bitch, if something needs doing in time you'll give it a stitch"

"What???"

"I have to admit that's not my best rhyme. I'm just getting used to it, give me time."

"Your accent keeps changing too."

"I know."

Empath Man tries to be encouraging.

"Nice hand movements you're doing there, Alan."

"Thanks."

Stewart's not mollified. "I'm getting really upset. You've no money, a crap phone. You've given Alan a creative gift, kind of …but what about me? What's my 'alternative currency' gift?"

"Well – you seem far more articulate and self-aware than at the beginning of the mugging"

Deep breath from Stewart. "That's part of my point. However grotesquely lucid I now am, my formerly simple feelings of generalised anger and acquisitiveness have grown in complexity in ways that outstrip my ability to articulate. Also, *technically* I don't think this qualifies as a mugging any more."

"I hear the excruciating irony that empowerment of my "empathic presence" is, for you, an amplification of feelings, without the mitigation of a creative or cathartic outlet."

"That's right!"

"You've hit the nail right on the head. If you hit it any harder the nail would be dead."

"You're just beginning to *really annoy me*, Alan"

"I'm finding my way with it. Just let me play with it."

"The fact is," Stewart turns back to Empath Man, "I still want to stab you."

"Maybe, for you, right now, stabbing is the best form of self-expression"

"How can I stab you? I have this weird relationship with you. It'd be like eating a family pet."

"Awww. That's one of the nicest reasons for not stabbing me anyone's ever given."

"Plus my rhyming friend here would probably come in on your side…"

"I don't think I would. I'd like a bit of a rumpus. Rhymin' don't make me good. I still lack a moral compass."

"Maybe I'll just stab you a bit to express my acute dismay at the terrible gap between my potential and the life mapped out for me by the indifference and assumptions of others."

"That's really well put."

"Thanks. I'm beginning to really like you"

"Will you still be able to stab me?"

"Yes. In the leg. And it's going to hurt"

"Okay, that's aaarrggghhh …really sore, but if it helps take the edge off unbearable feelings…"

"It's making it worse. Seeing your pain, your trusting innocence, reminds me of my own early years …only now I'm the one with the power, doing the punishing…"

"It's not helping?"

"Not really, maybe if I stabbed you harder, and twisted a little bit?"

"Actually. … There's another way. You see this bulge in my

pocket? It's oil pastels and some acrylics. You could express visually what you can't express through the medium of stabbing"

Stewart shrugs, "What have I got to lose?"

"Well, you may lose a redundant image of yourself as a low-achiever or uncreative person…"

"It was a rhetorical question"

"Sorry. I'm bleeding quite heavily"

"Yeah, whatever – look, I've got a lot I need to express here. Do you have any paper?"

"No, but here's a blank stretch of wall."

"Right, okay, give me the art stuff. You hold the knife."

Empath Man holds the knife. He and Alan look on, mesmerised, as Stewart puts all of himself into making his inner landscape visible on the cold render. They make appreciative noises and head movements…

Without looking round Stewart says, "Can you tell what I feel yet?"

"It's amazing. Those desolate blues, those jagged orange-reds. Fragile yet robust. Tender yet vicious. A fusion of resentment and redemption that's at once revolutionary and yet… …could make lovely wrapping paper."

"When you started out I thought the wall looked duller, but now I can see you've got a way with colour."

"Thanks guys. I'm just making marks from a true place inside. Hey mister, you seem to be losing a lot of blood – could I, um, use a bit….?"

"Help yourself."

They hear footsteps. "There's footsteps Stewart, you better stop, you never know who it might be… ooh, it's a cop"

"What's going on here then?" Empath Man, deathly pale, knife in hand, turns to the policeman.

"I take full responsibility, Officer. I can explain everything"

"Well then, why don't you?"

Empath Man seems incapable of further speech, so Alan chips in helpfully...

"He's given me the gift of verse and he's given Stewart some paint, but his bleedin' has bin gettin' worse – I think he's gonna faint..."

Empath Man faints.

UP SIGNATURE TUNE

Will Empath Man regain consciousness and explain everything? Or anything?

Will his blood work with acrylics and oil pastels?

Can art ever be therapy or vice versa?

Isn't that the wall of the Azkabhanistan Embassy?

All these questions will be swept aside in the excitement of the next episode of the continuing adventures of Empath Man!

Episode 2: From Court to Cult

Springing the Police Chief's daughter from a dodgy organisation is not without its trials

In the last moving episode of Empath Man our ultra-sensitive superhero awakened in two muggers their latent abilities as performance poet and abstract artist. Having first supported one through an experimental phase of self-expression through the medium of stabbing, he then offered his own blood as an art material and lost consciousness under questioning from a police officer. But not before taking responsibility for everything and saying that he could explain.

It's following his failure to explain that we join him in court, where the Judge seems, I don't know, kind of grumpy.

"Who is the prisoner and why is he brought before me?"

"The defendant, Mr M Pathman, is charged with inciting youngsters to vandalism, to whit to deface the wall of the Azkhabanistan Embassy in Sharedneedle Street. He is also charged with gratuitous self-harming in a public place, starting an artistic movement without due care and attention, and fainting in the presence of a police officer."

"These are not all proper charges are they?"

"No, m'lud. The defendant has an effect on people. The officer drawing up the charge sheet began to... ...express himself."

"Express himself?"

"Yes, m'lud. Under the influence of the defendant". The judge looks almost interested.

"So, Mr Pathman. It seems you are a man of influence. How do you plead?"

"That's difficult your honour. I can see I kind of did what they said, but I don't *feel* guilty – I feel more a relaxed, ambient acceptance of what's happened alongside a willingness to embrace what happens next – whether I feel like the author of what happens, or simply a water-boatman bobbing in the ripples from a pebble dropped by the hand of another."

The judge stirred. "Stenographer, strike the water-boatman imagery from the record. Mr Pathman, there's no such plea as 'ambient acceptance'. Guilty or not guilty."

"It's all so black and white with you. *Either/or.* I honestly feel both Guilty *and* Not Guilty

"I – and indeed the law – am not asking you how you feel, but how you plead"

"I couldn't feel one thing and plead another. Not under oath.

"You carry on like this, Mr Pathman, I'll have you for Contempt."

"Well, I'd have to plead not guilty to that. I have the highest esteem for this court, and everyone in it. From the humble stenographer to your exalted and judgmental self."

"Stenographer are you getting all this down?"

"Some of it, your honour"

"Some of it?"

"Um, I'm also having some thoughts of my own which seem … of value"

"You're recording your *own thoughts* on the case?"

"Not just the case, m'lud, on *things generally,* the tragedy and waste that passes before me here in the court, and positive things too, the necessity for boundaries in public life, the beauty of the sunlight on your honour's shiny gavel-handle. Little magic poemy things that pop into my head."

"Oh God"

"It's a new thing for me. I was hoping your honour would be more supportive."

"Enough. In a strange, sad way you bring us back to the charges against Mr Pathman. Mr Pathman, I am beginning to see for myself the insidious effect you have on people. They're not themselves around you"

"Objection, m'lud. People are *more* themselves around me."

"But you accept that you affect them. And played your part in the creation of the young 'artists'?"

"I suppose so. I was just trying to do my bit, you know, for society."

"So do you feel, Mr Pathman, that society *needs* more artists and performance poets?"

"Well… more than it needs muggers and ju…"

"Muggers and what? You were going to say something else, weren't you?"

"I don't want to tell you on the grounds that it would tend to hurt your feelings."

"Never mind my feelings, Pathman"

"I can't help it. It's one of the few parts of my identity that remains constant"

"You were going to say: society needs artists and performance poets more than it needs muggers and judges"

"I was, but, you know, it's not something that I necessarily stand by – I hadn't really thought it through…"

"But I have. And it's true. I know what I'm saying. I'm a judge. And everyone has to listen to me. Or you'll all go to prison."

"But.. you.. you don't really mean that!"

"No, it was a joke. Just because you're not laughing doesn't mean I'm not joking."

"Oh!"

"That was another joke."

"Ah! It's amazing, M'lud, even with my super-advanced empathic antennae, I can't tell when you're joking!"

"But it's true. Since I've met you I feel, I don't know the word for what I feel, I think I feel… …non-judgmental. That effect you have, it's working on me. I can't judge people any more. I won't. I'm going to hang up my wig, bury my gavel, step down and open up."

"Gosh!"

"I'm going to stop hiding behind the law. I'm going to get out more. And meet people."

"Crikey!"

"But before I do I'm going to pass sentence one last time."

"Objection, M'Lud!"

"Who are you?"

"Counsel for the Prosecution"

"And what's your objection?"

"I haven't had a chance to prosecute him, and… and… I'm just feeling really left out, and…"

"And….?"

"And, um, I also feel Guilty and Not-Guilty most of the time"

"Well said. Me too. Objection sustained *and* over-ruled"

"Wow – nice ruling!"

"I shall now pass sentence"

"…but there's been no verdict"

"There's no need. You're guilty as hell, and you're not-guilty as hell, too, and it's tough. I sentence you to Community Service…"

"Oh that's not so bad"

"…for a term not less than the rest of your natural life."

"But, but… I don't understand…"

"You will, Mr PathMan. With my last act of public service, I sentence you to walk from this court a free man – and yet not a free man. I sentence you to go forth and wreak your tender havoc, to walk your muddled well-meaning path and turn the mixed blessing of your gaze upon all you meet. Even if it's quite upsetting for them."

It's rare to see Empath Man so nonplussed. "But… where do I start?"

"I don't know. Ask a policeman. Now clear the court. I want to spend some quality time with my stenographer."

So Empath Man leaves the court, not entirely a free man. But, perhaps more important, a man with a focus. He takes to hanging around Scotland Yard. Where his presence makes the Police Chief feel uncomfortable.

We catch up with him in the Police Chief's office.

"Empath Man?"

"I'm here for you Chief"

"Yeah, whatever. Empath Man, we've got a cult problem."

"I hear your underlying urgency, Chief. Tell me more."

"There's not much more to tell."

"There's a tension in your voice, chief. This is about more than wanting to see gullible punters spared a financial and spiritual fleecing from a charismatic yet unscrupulous, power-crazed yet irresponsible charlatan. (BEAT) Isn't it?"

"I don't have time to go into detail, Empath Man."

"You can hide things from me, Chief. But you can't hide that you're hiding things from me. (BEAT) Do you have a daughter in that cult?"

"Damn you, you're not supposed to be psychic, Empath Man"

"I'm not, chief, I'm just emotionally open and I can read the signs. I couldn't help noticing when I came in you were holding a photo of your daughter, weeping softly and muttering "come back to me, come back.""

"Damn it, I didn't want you to see me like that."

"It's how I've always seen you, Chief. Don't worry – I hear your pain, your embarrassment and your irritation. How about a hug?"

"Don't touch me, Empath Man, or I'll break you like I've broken every other touchy-feely freak who's tried their psycho-fetish weirdness on me."

"Appreciate the straight-talk Chief. Guess I'll let my instinct for self-preservation outweigh my urge to reach out to you."

"Wise decision. Hey, maybe you will get a hug if you bring back my daughter, alive and clean. Until then you'll have to make do with this matey punch on the arm."

"Ouch. You pay in a strange currency Chief, but I accept you for the complex, brutal, trembling creature you are..."

"Get out of my office, Empath Man."

"Right Chief . Oh, and, um, Thanks"

"Thanks? Thanks for what?"

"For letting me in. For showing me the wounded, tender side of a tough, in-control man's man."

"I'm not letting you in Empath Man, I'm chucking you out."

"Whatever you say, Chief."

"You bring my daughter back, Empath Man, or I'll, I'll, god help me I don't know what I'll do"

"You'll continue to miss her, Chief, and torture yourself with how you never managed to translate your loving feelings into effective loving behaviour"

"Okay, I'm pointing my weapon at you now, Empath Man"

"Point taken, Chief. Adios"

"Adios, Empath Man. You're a good man, but you make my skin crawl."

"That's what they all say, Chief. Especially Stella."

So Empath Man turns up at the Cult HQ, or the Centre for Universal Light and Truth, and knocks on the door. It's answered by a thin guy in a white sarong. He looks cool, calm and collected.

"Hello, this is the Centre for Universal Light and Truth. What can I do for you?"

"I'm not sure. Is there anything I can do for you?"

"No. All my needs are met."

"You certainly seem to emanate a peace, confidence and radiant humility that's rare to find in a built-up area within two miles of a famous fast-food franchise"

"Thank you. So, what can I do for *you*?"

"I'm looking for something that's hard to put a name on."

"Try"

"Okay, um, I guess I'm looking for acceptance and belonging, an opportunity to both "find" and "lose" my "self""

"Anything else?"

"Yes, I'm also looking for um, for a path of simplicity and authenticity, preferably one defined and prescribed by a charismatic father/teacher figure, at once ubiquitous and remote, intimate yet elusive, free of material needs yet paradoxically grasping."

"I think you'd better come in…"

Empath Man steps inside the threshold of C.U.L.T. Headquarters. Into the cool, dimly lit foyer.

"My name is Partner 319, what's yours?"

"I, I, I'd rather not say right now"

"Welcome anyway, stuttering stranger, you are warmly invited to divest yourself of the worldly burdens that you carry."

"Worldly burdens?"

"Oh, you know, anxiety, body dismorphic disorder, high disposable income possibly linked to feelings of unworthiness…"

"Hmmmmm. Your words could sound sinister, yet my emotional antennae are picking up friendliness with gentle teasing. Are you aware that the initials of your organisation spell out the acronym CULT?"

"I am, and so is He."

"Did you say, "and so is He" with a capital *aitch*?"

"I did. You have a problem with that?"

"To be honest I do, but alongside my other problems it seems pretty insignificant."

"So, you're a guy with significant problems."

"Maybe. But I like to think I'm bigger than my personal problems. I've come here on a mission."

A figure steps out from the shadows. In the reception area. A slight figure but with undeniable presence. It's Mr LightBringer, aka Partner no 1.

"A mission? We're all here on a mission, Empath Man…"

Empath man blinks. "How do you know my name? I came here under cover."

"Much that is hidden is known to me, and much that is known to me is hidden."

"Oh, nice." Partner 319 pulls out a notebook. "I'll write that one down, for the blog. Partner No 1 is so wise he creates branding reinforcement opportunities just by opening his mouth …"

"Enough!" Partner no. 1 looks almost sheepish. "Our visitor will think you're sycophantic poodles rather than strong-willed individuals who happen to have chosen the path of truth over the superficial satisfactions of well-paid work and supportive relationships with family and friends…"

"Who are you?"

"You ask who He is, can you not feel His presence? A power that is peaceful, a softness that is strong, a poetic imagination that is surprisingly good with figures…"

"Enough, allow our new member to form his *own* impressions"

"I'm not your new member, Mr Light-Bringer"

"And yet you are here, among us, with your problems, your hopes, dreams, fears, your bank account details, including pin number and internet passwords…"

"Ha ha, see how Partner no. 1 plays non-judgementally with the new member's preconceptions and expectations… and uses irony as a healing tool – marvellous"

"*Are* you using irony as a healing tool, Mr LightBringer?"

"That's not for me to say, Empath Man. How do you feel?"

"No-one ever asks me how I feel… It's strange but I do feel a …healing presence. I feel relaxed, comfortable. Nor do I feel judged for coming here under cover, although kind of I judge myself…"

"You judge yourself?"

"I feel ungracious, I came here to expose you, but it is I who am exposed, my own cynicism and suspicion. [No wonder Stella doesn't want anything to do with me.]"

"Indeed" Mr Light-Bringer nods knowingly as Empath Man gushes on.

"I'm so impressed by your winning combination of innocence and irony…"

"We call it 'ironocence'™"

"Ironocence™ – I see what you did there! … a new word made by joining innocence and irony, thus opening new channels in my heart and mind. Wonderful. I see now that when you ask me for my bank details you are joking, and yet…"

"…yes, deadly serious at the same time"

"Beautiful, beautiful. But I must not be too easily swayed. I must ask the hard questions. Surely for all your "ironocence"™ you are nevertheless exploiting your so-called partners?"

"How? You feel their peace, joy, savour their gentle teasing…?"

"I do it's true, but I was thinking maybe financially?"

"How, when I am but a partner – and any cheque I sign is only valid when counter-signed by a vulnerable person with whom I'm having inappropriate sexual relations…"

"I see that I have much to learn about authenticity and simple human trust. But it's my duty to maintain a last sliver of mistrust… I made a promise – I must ask to see the Police Chief's daughter…"

"I'm afraid she cannot see you…"

"So, my sliver is well-founded…"

"… *because* she is at the local community college, studying part-time for an MBA in Business Studies"

"Ah my last sordid residue of suspicion evaporates in the warm of the C.U.L.T. Ironocence™ culture. What's happening to me? I'm flapping and fluttering inside like the ordinary guy I used to be before I became what I… never asked to be… I feel I've found something I didn't even know I was looking for – I've never experienced such turmoil and peace at the same time, or such an overwhelming urge to tell someone my PIN number…"

UP SIGNATURE TUNE

Has Empath Man been so easily swayed from his mission to rescue the Police Chief's daughter?

Has he truly found something of lasting and intrinsic worth with "ironocence"™?

Will he really give up his bank details and PIN number to a shadowy figure with no outward signs of probity?

Find out in the next unnerving episode of Empath Man…

Episode 3: Hot Air Rises

Having excelled as a cult-buster, Empath Man falls into the clutches of his nemesis, the dangerously charming Scorpio Rising.

…Last episode saw Empath Man sentenced to community service for life in the last judgement of a judge who'd been rendered non-judgmental. He was tasked by the Police Chief to rescue his daughter from a dubious cult – and when we last saw him he was so won over by the leader, Mr Light-Bringer, he was experiencing a turmoil and a peace that he'd never known before and was on the verge of symbolically handing over his bank details and PIN number.

We catch up with him in the reception area of CULT HQ, with Mr Light-Bringer, Partner 319 and a clutch of curious cult members. Empath Man is finishing his initiation into the cult. He's just given his bank details and PIN number.

"Thank-you", says Mr Light-Bringer, "last but not least, internet passwords, "

"Ah"

"Problem?"

"I feel a bit shy"

"We're all adults, blurt it out"

"StellaComeBack and StellaComeBackILOVEYou. LOVE in upper case." Empath Man heaves a heartfelt sigh. "It's such a relief, I can't tell you."

"Better out than in"

"I know it's just symbolic – but it's what it symbolises: separateness, isolation. I never asked to be a superhero, you know."

"Awww. Poor old you."

"I know I should be grateful but sometimes I wish I could tuck away my emotional antennae, like a doctor takes off her stethoscope or a fireman rolls up his hose..."

There is the distant sound of Pan Pipes of the Andes "...oh, excuse me, that's my mobile... Hello Chief, how are you?"

"Never mind that. What about Helvetica?"

"Who?"

"My daughter. Have you seen Helvetica?"

"Good news, Chief. Your daughter's in good hands. The CULT is excellent. I've just joined it.

"Have you taken leave of your senses Empath Man?"

"Not at all. I'm picking up that you're very angry – with me, your daughter, the cult, in fact the whole world"

"You've lost it Empath Man. I'm coming over.

"Is that a wise course in your inflamed state, Chief? Oh, he's hung up."

A young woman enters – looks like a student.

"What's this I hear about a new member?"

"Hello you must be Helvetica, the Police Chief's Daughter."

"No-one calls me that except Daddy."

"Yes, he sent me to bust the cult and fetch you but I joined the cult and then he phoned and I told him you were fine and he said he's coming over. He seemed cross."

"That's daddy! Tch! He must really care about me. Gosh, what powerful daddy-based feelings are coming up in me..."

"Yes, "Empath Man sighs, "this is what happens. But... oh!" Suddenly his eyes widen. "Do you know what... I've got strong feelings – leader-based feelings – coming up in me, too. Wow, I'm actually feeling mistrust, and... something else... not exactly a feeling... good god, there's a rational function kicking in. I must thank you Mr Light-Bringer, this is amazing...

"Don't mention it," the cult leader frowned," ...for a moment there I thought you were going to try to *expose* me."

"Ah, yes, sorry, I'm afraid I must now expose you for the fraudulent fraud that you are…"

"What?"

"You heard me correctly"

"Do you realise the double negative, fraudulent fraud, implies I'm actually the real thing!"

"Yes, I'm saying you're a fraudulent fraud, but not in the sense you mean – you're a double fraud, with layers of fraudulence unknown even to yourself."

The cult members find it all difficult to follow. "We're getting a bit lost". Their leader's next comment doesn't help.

"Then you're saying I'm an *innocently* fraudulent fraud"

"Paradoxically, yes."

"You can't use paradox against me, Empath Man. I am paradox."

"And yet you're not…" [Sharp intake of breath.] The cult members don't like the way this is going. Empath Man presses on, "Listen Light-Bringer, there is something on the emotional event horizon I think you should know about…"

Partner no 319 gasps, "Oh my god Empath Man's deploying Advanced Empathy…."

"What could there possibly be. You can't expose me. Compassionate corruption is my USP. What's left to expose?"

"It's not what, it's *who*"

"What?"

"I'm going to expose you to yourself. There's more to you than meets the eye. You have a conscience, Mr Light-Bringer. It's waking as we speak. It's coming looking for you."

"Conscience? Have you lost your mind? If I had a conscience how could I do what I do, how could I be what I, am I mean how could I possibly, how *could* I? what? Oh my God, What have I done? How could I have done it? what's happening? …..oh my God it's kicking in. I feel, I feel…. guilt, shame, remorse… stop it Empath Man, make it go away…"

Empath Man is helpless. "There's nothing I can do – I'm just the weatherman…"

The tragic leader looks around desperately. "I can't… I'm sorry… I've got to go." As he runs from the building he calls over his shoulder, "I'm really, really sorry, I should have known better…"

Silence, punctuated by sniffles from bereft former cult members. Then a man rushes in, brandishing a truncheon.

"Okay, Police Chief here, what's happening? Who was that man running away in distress, with a surprisingly responsible, concerned look on his face?"

Former Partner 319: "That was our former-leader who Empath Man has just awakened, through his presence, to the existence of a conscience that was dormant but not dead. If I've understood everything correctly."

"Good work." The Chief looks almost mollified. "Perhaps I've been over-hasty in coming here armed to the teeth and in a filthy temper."

Empath Man smiles wryly. "Tch! How often have I heard that said!"

"But what about us?" It's the dejected Cult members "You can't leave us. We are clumsy, awkward creatures, lost puppies of uncertainty…"

"I must leave you, the time has come for you to stand on your own all fours."

"You took Partner no 1 from us. You have a duty of care – you are the milky bottle of hope and we wish to suckle on your plastic teat."

"Your imagery makes me uncomfortable, but you have a point. I won't be your leader, but I have a suggestion: You could re-constitute the cult as a co-operative. Tweak, very slightly, your techniques of grooming, induction and brain-washing, and sell courses in self-development and team-building to the corporate sector…"

"Thank you Empath Man. By reframing our skills shortage as a positive commodity you have transformed us from idealistic-yet-inadequate cult-fodder to corporate consultancy parasites, thus restoring our dignity and earning potential."

Empath Man shrugs, "Don't mention it."

Helvetica steps forward. "I thank you too Empath Man. I see now that running away, joining a cult and starting a business studies course was just a way of getting Daddy's attention. From now on I shall get it through promotion and marketing, brand recognition and crushing my business rivals – like a normal, healthy girl."

"That's my girl! Well, Empath Man, you've busted the cult, you've re-united Helvetica and me, how can we possibly thank you?"

"You could get me Stella's contact details"

"I'm sorry, no can do Empath Man, it's unethical"

"I'm already morally compromised, Chief. I do what's necessary to keep things tidy"

"Don't put yourself down, Empath Man. We all respect the hell out of you."

"Guess I'll just have to make do with the shallow, fleeting adulation of those whose values are temporarily skewed by a sense of narrative gratification. Not the most nutritious emotional diet, but I'll take what junk-food I can find."

"Well, maybe you'd like that hug I promised you earlier."

"I never thought I'd say no to a hug, Chief, certainly not one from you, but I guess I'm not ready for male on male upper body intimacy so soon after giving my bank details to people who lack a moral compass. A manly handshake will suffice."

"I'm relieved to hear you say that, Empath Man. But hey, maybe there's something you are ready for. Would you like to join my Men's Group?"

"Wow – there's something I never thought I'd hear, Chief. Your *men's group?*"

"It's one of the longest running, pre-dates the feminist movement by hundreds of years…"

"You don't mean… ?"

"Yes. I'm asking you to join the Masons. I mean it, Empath Man"

"I know you do, Chief, because this is the longest we've ever maintained eye contact. My God, I know it's on the rebound from a dubious cult-joining experience, but I'm a sucker for a secret ritual. I'd love to join your Men's Group."

"Great. We'll be in touch."

So. Another day, another job. A father re-united with his daughter. A scoundrel with his conscience. And a bunch of unworldly gullible people with what passes for the real world.

Now he walks home, alone, reflecting on the twists his life has taken since he took part in the drugs trial for pharmaceuticals giant EctoGriffTwine… and mutters to himself, half under his breath, in that irritating way he has.

"How does that song go? 'Alone again. Naturally.' I never realised how deep Gilbert O'Sullivan really is. Now I know too well. 'You're a bad dog, baby, but I still want you around, around, around…' What a guy. He's been there – he knows."

Meanwhile, not far above in the overcast sky, unbeknownst to our hero, a hot air balloon hovers, and a shapely shadowy figure monitors his movements.

"Is that him?"

"It's him, ma'am"

"Okay. Lower me down there, on that multi-storey car park. Be ready."

"Wilco, ma'am"

Oblivious to this covert interest, Empath Man monologues on:

"Guess I shouldn't feel sorry for myself. I have my advanced listening skills, and my imperfect but exceptionally sensitive emotional antennae. OK I never asked for these powers. But then: Did the shark ask for his teeth? Did trees ask to have leaves? God I miss Stella. And not just emotionally.

This monologue isn't really helping. Look there's a crowd gathered ahead. They're all looking up. Maybe there's a beautiful moon…"

Soon he's close enough to make out individual voices in the crowd.

"There's a woman up there! She's leaning forwards. Oh my god! She's gonna jump!"

"She's leaning back. She's bending… sideways, and stretching. She's doing yoga!"

"I can see her knickers! It's a leotard. Doesn't count."

"She's not going to jump," They sound disappointed. "She's just doing bendy health stretches."

"Despair makes you very flexible, I've read that. It was in the Guardian."

"Hey, it's Empath Man. Empath Man, over here, we need you!"

"Hi, guys, lovely evening"

"There's a woman up on the multi-storey."

"Yes, she seems to be doing yoga. Weird, isn't it? People! Tch!"

"We're really worried."

"Understandable, but while she is both enigmatic and daring, all my antennae are picking up is a quiet confidence coupled with sensual pleasure in her own physicality."

"We're still *really* worried. Couldn't you just save her – for us?"

"Actually I've just come off-duty."

"Ha, ha. Nice that you can joke with us. But while she's up there, in danger, it's ethically a bit dubious, we think"

"No, really, I'm off-duty."

"You can't be off-duty. You're a natural phenomenon. Like the wind, and the internet."

"Am I? My wife Stella says all the amplification of emotion is unnatural. She finds it creepy."

"We do too, to be honest, but it's a natural organic creepiness, like outdoor spiders."

"Oh, great. Thanks."

Some are still watching the stretchy woman. "She's building up to it. She's waiting for a decent crowd to form, then she'll jump."

"Then why don't you just disperse?"

"I'm an individual. I can't disperse."

"I was talking to the crowd as a whole."

"Oh."

"C'mon" a lone voice pipes up, "We'll report you. To the Advertising Standards Authority. And to Ofcom"

"What?"

"You're Empath Man: 'Always on call'. 'A man you can rely on' with a shoulder you can cry on'

"But I don't advertise!"

"Well, you seem very uncaring for a superhero whose USP is compassionate listening."

"Oh for crying out loud. I'm going up, not because she needs saving, or because of my sentence, but because she's interesting and attractive, and because you're beginning to wind me up!"

"Eeeeooouuuuuggghhhh!" The crowd make handbag gestures "Get him!" "Sponge-bag!"

Empath Man ignores them, shaking his head as he strides up the multi-storey. "Honestly, crowds, they're so childish." So he misses the exchange between two crowd members...

"Hey, isn't that a hot-air balloon up there?" "Oh yeah"

Empath Man emerges onto the roof, strolls tentatively toward the woman.

"Hi, nice night for a stretch, how are you doing?"

"Just fine. Who wants to know?"

"Just a... passer-by"

"A passer-by?"

"Yep"

"But you didn't pass by, did you?"

"Nope"

"You came up."

"Yep"

"I like a man who's willing to... ...come up."

Empath Man gulps

"Do you have a name?"

He nods

"Don't tell me. Would it be… The Empath Kid?"

"Man, actually"

"I'll call you Kid, until you give me good reason to upgrade you. So, Kid, do you like my stretching?"

"Are you flirting with me?"

"Flirting? What do you mean?"

"Um, behaving in a playful and alluring way, especially one that gives the impression of sexual interest…"

"You tell me, Kid. What are your *emotional antennae* telling you?"

"It's hard to say – it's as if the blood has drained out of them…"

"Mmm… I wonder where it could have gone…"

"I'm sensing your motives are not pure"

"You better believe it, Kid"

"What's that noise?"

"That'll be my lift. My PA is a stickler for punctuality"

"Good God. It's a hot air balloon. With a rope ladder dangling from it."

"If you hadn't been so busy looking where you were looking you might have noticed it sooner."

"Yes, well… that's a really nice leotard."

"And you haven't asked me my name."

"Manners! What's your name?"

"Scorpio Rising and you'll never see me again unless you're willing to scale my ladder and climb into my basket"

"Gosh. Is this one of those 'honeytraps' I've heard about?"

"Bzzzzzzzzzzz" The crowd below are scandalised.

"He's climbing in the balloon with the alluring stretchy woman. That's got to be unethical."

"I'm accepting your invitation, Scorpio, but I want you to know that technically I am still married."

"Well Kid, technically bees are unable to fly…"

UP SIGNATURE TUNE

Are bees technically unable to fly?

How impure are Scorpio Rising's motives?

Will the blood flow back into Empath Man's antennae in time to rescue him from Scorpio's big wicker basket?

All these questions will be explored in depth in future adventures of…

…Empath Man

PUTTING IT ACROSS

Sometimes you don't realise you have any authority until you lose it. Then you find you had some all along, really. Up to a point. But of course, thinking you don't have it, you try to claim it. Then you lose it. And, in the process, realise you had actually had it, had you but known it, which of course you didn't, or you wouldn't have tried to claim it in the first place.

I'm not really management material, I don't think. Although I am, officially, the manager. I'm more Sven Goran Eriksson than Alex Ferguson. I don't throw teacups or kick equipment around. I don't even do sarcasm very well. I don't think they'd stand for it frankly. Not in over-35's football. Especially if you're under 35, like me. I turned up wanting to train with them till I was eligible to play. And they made me manager. Saw me coming.

I try to be positive. I try to motivate, say two positives for every negative. Sometimes three. Four maybe, but beyond that sounds like sarcasm.

Because we're not really a great team. We haven't got particularly good players. And some of them aren't very nice. They don't play as a team. They play *in* a team. They wear the same blue shirts and shorts – except Alan, who wears his number 9 Jimmy Floyd Hasselbaink Chelsea shirt. But it's like having the same kit isn't enough proof of identity for them to pass to one another. They need more – maybe a driving licence, a copy of their birth certificate. Or they need team mates to argue the case for passing to them, and maybe then they'll consider it. But by then it's too late. Or, more accurately, two nil.

Which was the score at half time. And I would have loved to have talked of issuing identity cards for proof of team membership, but I show restraint. I say, "You're better than this score-line", I say, "I've seen some good tackles going in, good passes, we need more than that." I say, "Keep your heads up", I say, "blah, blah, cliché, blah, blah, blah, cliché lads." And "stick at it."

And I don't honestly believe they pay any attention, although the nicer ones look up and nod, as if they were.

And today, in the second half, it was as if they were. They passed the ball, sometimes to each other. They tackled, sometimes in a non-girly way. They even scored. Twice. Pulled level. Unheard of. The travelling supporters couldn't believe it. The travelling supporters, by the way, are me and Stan. Stan the Fan. The Old Man of the Park. He adopted the team in the early days and they adopted him too, because there wasn't much else to do – a fan's a fan.

He doesn't say much, Stan – but, when he does, no-one listens. I feel a kinship with him. An unspoken kinship. Because what's the point?

With five minutes to go Stan and I get passionate. We hit the inside of the post but it bounces out and we shout, "Ref! Ref!" as if, when the laws of physics are flouted like that, he can over-rule what's happened and award a goal. But he lacks the courage and imagination.

Then, two minutes to go, a lucky ricochet falls to the feet of our centre forward, Alan. He knocks a defender over with his formidable upper body strength, gets away with it, looks up, the keeper's off his line. And Roger arrives in the box screaming for the ball – a simple ball for a simple goal – and Alan pauses, assesses the situation, and coolly, casually, with no backswing like his role model Jimmy Floyd Hasselbaink, and shoots, feebly, into the side-netting.

Stan and I are stunned. And bitter. We're stunned, bitter and speechless. We can't believe anyone, even Alan, would do that. There's a muttering from the touchline. "Typical. Just typical." That's Stan. There's another voice. "Irresponsible. It's downright irresponsible." That's me. And Stan looks at me and says,

"Someone's got to say something to that man." And I look back and I nod, as if to say, "Yes, the time has come. I'm the manager. Something has to be said."

I was going to say something in the dressing room. But it didn't feel right. So I waited till we were gathered in the bar of the Unigate Creamery Social Club. Then I realised I should have said something in the dressing room. I sit down opposite Alan. No preamble. Blurt out, "You should have put it across, Alan."

He just looks at me. Expressionless. An absence of menace that's intimidating. And I think, "Colin, you're an idiot. This is over-35's football. It's a laugh and a run-around. You're over-reacting. You're bringing it to the Crown Court when it's a Small Claims case. You're being ridiculous."

I'm about to back down, cravenly, when he says, "Across to who?"

"Across to who?" I say.

"Yeah", he says, "Across to who?"

I fight the impulse to say, "You mean: Across to whom?"

"Across to Roger", I say, nodding at Roger who's sat opposite nursing a fruit juice. We both look across to Roger.

"Yeah?" says Alan.

My case could collapse here as I realise my first witness is intimidated. But he admits it. "Yes, I was lurking in the box."

Alan considers this a moment, to Roger's discomfort. Then turns to me and to my discomfort says, "He should have called for it."

Without a witness protection scheme I can't expect Roger to volunteer further evidence.

I say, "Roger did call for it, Alan."

"Well he should have called louder."

"If he'd called any louder he'd have broken council bye laws. He'd have breached the peace!"

I'm trying to lighten things up. And failing.

Roger tried to smooth things. "It's all right", he says, "I'd have fluffed it anyway." I want him to shut up. But I don't say so. Alan shuts him up when he says, "It's obviously not all right, Roger, not for Colin."

And I feel the room go quiet, and the stakes go higher. Everyone knows something's happening. Something is being said.

Alan turns back to me. "Why didn't you say this in the dressing room?"

He's right. I should have said this in the dressing room. But then I couldn't, and now I have to. I can't explain. I shrug. "I'm saying it now."

He nods, as if that's quite a good point. "But why are you saying it, Colin? What's your point? What do you want?"

God this is hard. I've got to back off or plough on. I say, "It's not just about this one time, not crossing it. I want you to play for the team. Not just for Alan."

He says, "You know what I think, Colin?"

Which to me is a rhetorical question. But he pauses for so long I think I'd better answer. "No Alan, I don't. What do you think?"

"I think you've got a problem with Alan Parsons."

He's right. But that was the point.

"And," he goes on, "I think you've got to decide whether you want Alan Parsons in your team."

Heady stuff. *My* team. The highest status I'd ever had. And Alan Parsons has moved into the third person.

"Easy decision," I say. "I want Alan Parsons *in* the team – and *for* it."

Alan smiles sadly. Shakes his head. "You want to have your Alan Parsons and keep him."

I say, "What?"

He says, "What you want you can't have."

"Why not?"

"Because I am Alan Parsons."

"I know that Alan. I'm not disputing it. But can't Alan Parsons change, slightly? Doesn't Alan Parsons have a choice?"

Alan continues to surprise me. "Look," he says, "it's not whether I play for Alan or for the team. I play *as* Alan. I have Alan's ability. I have Alan's attitude. Because he is me. I am Alan."

He's suddenly earnest and surprisingly gentle. "Colin, I can't not be Alan."

The men around us, including some of the Unigate players, are listening openly now. They're gathered round us like a jury of twelve dull men and true. And they're nodding. I'm losing the argument.

I say, "Alan, I agree you are Alan. But as Alan I don't agree you have no choice. You have free will. You're a free man."

He looks at me. "Am I, Colin?"

It was good to be back in the first person. But it doesn't last.

"Colin, if I was the Alan you wanted, I wouldn't be the Alan I am."

Not only are we back in the third person, we're in a country song by Lyle Lovett. I'm sitting in Unigate Creamery Social Club in a country song scenario with a man old enough to be my financial advisor.

It's become clear to Alan the only reason I'm giving him a hard time is a simple lack of basic understanding. He says, "Colin, Colin. Colin, Colin, Colin. Football is an instinctive thing. It's a sublimation of battle. It's heat of the moment. It's instincts, reflexes. And for people like me, people like Jimmy Floyd, the sight of goal is like the scent of quarry. You know we evolved from hunter-gatherers, right?"

"Right."

"Well some people are more hunter than gatherer. Yeah?"

I'm not sure.

"Some are all hunter and no gatherer, and some are all gatherer and no hunter. Yeah?"

"I'm not sure, Alan."

"It's basic Darwinism, Colin. The sight of goal equals the smell of blood. In that moment it's not a football match. It's a hunt."

"A hunt?"

"Yes, a hunt!"

"Hunt isn't the first word that comes to mind, Alan."

I deeply regret saying that. But it was a heat of the moment thing. The smell of bullshit. He ignores it, but I know he's heard it.

"I'm sorry, Colin. The hunter is selfish. He doesn't explain. He doesn't apologise. That's how it is with me."

"And Jimmy Floyd," I said.

"And Jimmy Floyd."

"So that's why you don't track back or mark anyone. It's against your instincts."

He shrugs. "That's not an instinct thing. It's more of a principle."

"A principle."

I begin to feel sarcasm welling up in me. A visceral, unstoppable, evolutionary sarcasm. "Well, if it's a principle you should have said! I didn't realise I'd touched on a question of conscience. I see what you mean now. What choice do you have? Morally you have no choice. What you are really is a conscientious objector."

"I can respect a conscientious objector," I said. And straightaway wished I hadn't because 'respect' is a big word and I'd raised the stakes again. And my voice was getting louder while his was getting softer, and I didn't know how to finish the sentence without making things worse.

He didn't let me. "That's the difference between you and me, Colin. I don't respect conscientious objectors."

Oh dear. The goalposts have moved. We've as good as mentioned the war. Did he know where I stood on the war? Of course he did. I thought, "Don't go down that road. Move in, seize the goalposts, sum up and get out."

I said, "Alan, Alan, Alan, Alan, Alan." I said, "The difference between you and me, Alan, is about choice. It's about attitude, it's about choice. All I'm saying is it's your choice – whether you play for the team, for yourself, or just with yourself. It's your choice whether you admit you have a choice, or duck behind your daft, distorted Darwinism. It's your choice whether you're going to *be* Alan Parsons or a sub-Jimmy Floyd Hasselbaink clone. You're stuck with being Alan Parsons. The question is whether you're going to be responsible for him or just typical of him."

And I should have left it there. Because I felt I'd equalised. Maybe even scored the decider. I felt I was winning the battle for hearts and minds. But I said, unnecessarily, irrevocably, "What's it going to be, Alan?" And he had one more surprise up his sleeve.

He hit me. Hard. With no back swing. I was quick, but he was quicker. Catching my chin as I jerked back in my chair, which tilted, reached the point of balance, and slowly fell. Thud. Sending out ripples of silence through the Social Club.

Alan stood up and said, "That's the difference between you and me, Colin." Then he picked up his fleece and walked off.

Nobody laughed. Or applauded. Which was nice. I lay on my back in the chair, eyes closed. I felt things had slipped away from me. Perhaps I should resign, there and then, like Kevin

Keegan after Germany. I opened my eyes and saw Stan looking down at me. He nodded. "Well done, son. Someone had to say something."

"But he hit me, Stan."

Stan smiled a rare smile and, with helpful clarity underwritten with compassion, as if lifting the veil on the mystery of human motivation into which I'd just been ritually initiated, he said, "Yes, well. He would, wouldn't he?"

REGAINING THE ASHES

Dad said you could sum up our traditional family Christmases in four words: Bird, board, bicker and box. And he was right. The bird was always turkey; the board game progressed via Ludo, Cluedo and Monopoly to Scrabble where it's been ever since; the bickering would start during the board game then carry on intermittently until we settled in front of the box; where we'd watch Morecambe and Wise. We watched them in their heyday along with everyone else – then, thanks to video and dvd technology, every Christmas since.

Someone said once, "It's nice you all have the same sense of humour," and Dad said "Yes, except it means we have to take it in turns to laugh." Which I think is one of his better jokes. Of which there aren't many.

Now it's just Jenny and me - and Dad, sort of - keeping the traditions going. Three out of four traditions. We're not doing the bird bit - she's got a new bloke and she's spending Christmas evening with his family. But she wouldn't miss the board bit with me. She turns up on time, with Dad, naturally, we exchange a few pleasantries then we get straight to it.

The Annual Christmas Custody Challenge. House rules. No blanks. What Chambers says goes. Christmas-link bonus at opponent's discretion. We're off. She wins the toss - well, she picks a 'p' (worth 3) to my 'o' (worth 1) so she's first to the crease with PRAISE - 'p' on the double letter. I grant the 5-point bonus for the Praise the Lord Christmas theme, she's off the mark with 27. I respond with FLOOR, double word score, 16, early days, all to play for. Her next word MOW, even with the 'w' on the triple letter, disappoints. It gives her 16 and me hope. Which I need, frankly.

According to Dad hope's what Christmas is all about. Christmas was Christmas long before it was called Christmas, he said. It's the festival of light in the darkness, the hope that life will return. Those in the know saying to those who aren't so confident: Life goes on.

Don't worry your primitive little heads about it. That's why, he said, Morecambe and Wise always finish with Bring Me Sunshine. It's basically a pagan affirmation of the continuity of life, and the values of hope and happiness in the face of cold and dark. I know that's not 100% true or rational, but it works for me.

I make NUKED, which isn't pretty, and Jenny the purist doesn't like it, but it's in the dictionary. I even claim a Christmas bonus, because of the nuclear tests on Christmas Island, but she won't have it. She makes SHIRT with the 's' on MOWS for 22.

Not the best use of an 's' to my mind. I sense she's off form, distracted perhaps by thoughts of Mr NewBloke. I risk opening up the board and exposing the triple word score with WEAPON. Gives me a symbolic lead of 7. More importantly I pick up the 'q'.

I look across at Dad. Sat there, uncomplaining, disinterested. A trophy Dad, in a way. Beyond it all yet in the thick of it. It's only really when he's here I realise how much I miss him. Traditions are strange things. Dad said tradition is doing what we do now because it's what we did then. Whether or not it's a good idea now. Whether or not it was a good idea then. Precedent outranks practicality, he said. And sanity, he should have said. At some point Dad tempered and ritualised post-bird board-game bickering by interviewing us, like a TV commentator, during and after the game. He'd hold a banana, ask Richard and Judy-type questions and we would air our grievances into the banana, share our thoughts, give quite detailed and eloquent answers. Only occasionally seizing it from him and stamping out of the room. It's odd how quickly this tradition stopped seeming odd, became just what we did.

It's not always clear where traditions come from, but he started that one, and I started this one. I suggested it – admittedly with the emphasis on jest. I collected the ashes from the crematorium, I was supposed to hand them to Jenny. I didn't want to. I didn't understand my own hesitation. "I know," I said, "as a tribute to Dad we should play Scrabble for his Ashes. House rules. The winner to keep them for the year – on display, hidden away, whatever — next year, on Christmas Day, we play again." She took me by surprise when she said, "Hmm, yes. Like the cricket." "Yes," I said. "It's probably what he would have wanted" she said. "Yes," I said. "Of course Mum wouldn't have approved," she said. "No," I said. "He'd have liked that," she said. "Yes," I said.

That's how I talked her into it. So I can't say it's not my fault because it is and I know it is. And now Jenny and me have kept it up for ten years. Christmas Day Scrabble, winner take all. All, of course, being Dad, or what's left of him. We used to play with him, now we play for him. What kind of people are we? I say this last bit out loud. She says, "We're word-based organisms," and puts an 's' at the end of WEAPON, signalling her intent to attack the triple. It's not a question of whether, the 's' says, but how. "You're playing with me," I say. "Yep," she says, "That's the idea." And makes JOUST with 'J' on the double letter. 72 points. What can you say?

What I say is, "Good use of the 'j', Jenny". I can afford to be gracious. I have a 'q', I have a 'u' I have an 'a' 'l' 'i' 't' 'y'. Oh my word. "Jenny," I say, "I'm glad you're here to share this moment." I place the 'y' on the end of shirt and work backwards, 't', 'i', 'l', 'a', 'u', 'q'. QUALITY. She just looks at it, doesn't start adding up. "It's got quality written all over it," I say. She frowns. "I'm not sure about shirty." "Don't get shirty about shirty, shorty," I say. "I'm not," she says. "And don't get shifty about being shirty about it," I say, "or I'll give you short shrift." "Shut up," she says. Being irritating like this is tactics on my part, not scrabble tactics exactly but wider, off-board tactics. I'm practising what's known as One-Downsmanship. By those who know.

She thinks for ages and ages, then puts down PALLET. 16 points. Not a great response. Don't get complacent I tell myself, complacently. I make OPENING, opening up the lower right quadrant of the board for 22. You can't relax against this level of opposition. Out of nowhere she produces BATIQUE (batique!) with the 'q' of QUALITY. Triple word, 57, game on. I respond well, I use the 'b' for BY and make BEVY. It's in the dictionary. Plus a Christmas-link bonus for 32. She does some tight work with an 'x'. OF, FOX and EX for 27. God she's good.

I see her gaze flick across to Dad. Eyes on the prize. It amazes me to think we actually did it, but we did, we still do. And for a year or two we felt big, clever and funny, maybe three or four, but then I began to feel uneasy. And the more uneasy I felt the more she felt comfortable, settled and secure in our latest tradition. Helped of course by the fact that since I won the inaugural test she's had nine straight wins in a row. But what can you do? Well, you can bicker.

So Jenny and I had an argument about it. She won. Firstly, she said, it was my idea, secondly I was just a poor loser, thirdly she missed Dad too and playing for his Ashes was a way of keeping his memory alive, and fourthly it was a tradition. I told her what Dad said about tradition. She said, "Dad said, Dad said, I don't want to hear what Dad said, I just want to play Scrabble for his ashes on Christmas Day – *like we always do.*"

And this combination of passion and precedent seemed irrefutable. I couldn't argue so I did the next best thing, I sulked. I may have lost the argument, but I like to think I won the sulk. It was a good, creative, fruitful sulk. I complained to Dad, directly in my head. Here's another fine mess I've got you into, I said. And he smiled, in my head. And we had a conversation, in my head. Several conversations – I think it's okay to do that – and afterwards I knew what I had to do. Or at least what I was going to do.

I had a little bonfire, a ritual one. I burnt a Scrabble set, a set
of stumps, bails, bat and ball, all quite cheap. I burnt several
Patrick O'Brian novels, some Dick Francis a couple of Terry
Pratchett and a PD James. I burnt some old shoes. I wanted the
replacement ashes to have real meaning. I put them in a sizeable
jiffy bag. All I have to do now, I thought, is win back the Ashes.
That was three years ago. I've not had the run of the letters. I
take succour from England's win this Summer. If they can do it
so can I. I give myself little pep talks. I see every word as a little
innings in its own right.

I'm thinking these things and playing with my letters. I have a
precious 's' which will go on the end of OPENING. And a 'v'. I
can almost make VARIOUS, SAVOURY, no, ARISE, crap, or …
OVARIES. Yes. Ovaries and openings, All my letters, 74. I even
ask for the Christmas-link bonus?" "Why?" she says. "The virgin
birth," I say. "Twerp"' she says, and hits back with CALM - the
'm' on the triple-word. Claims Christmas bonus on the grounds
of 'All is calm, all is bright'.

I grant it, which surprises her. She looks up. I must look smug.
Surely I can't surpass my own OVARIES. I can. Around the 'm'
of CALM I make AMNIOTIC. Yes. A hat-trick of 50 point all-
letter bonuses. I punch the air, silently, in slow motion. As Dad
would have done. "Chip off the old block," she says. "Flintoff
the old block, more like," I say. Which *must* be irritating. But she
doesn't respond. I'm trying to get the bickering underway and
she's not making it easy.

She hasn't given up. She makes VENEER with the 'n' of
NUKED, exposing the triple. I spoil its potential with a cynical
NAÏVE. Mixing my sporting metaphors, this is equivalent to
taking the ball to the corner flag. When she's behind she's like a
wounded animal with a frightening vocabulary and while there's
a Z out there she's dangerous. She proves this with BRAZEN.
Even so her 43 hardly dents the plush cushion of my lead. I
make DRY and BY for 28. Hardly any letters left.

She makes GOD on the triple in the top left. I check the scores.
I give her a Christmas bonus for God himself and another for
the subtle underlying reference to the trinity. I can afford to. I've
won. We use up the last letter, and she adds up the total scores.
I bring out the banana and start the interviews. "So, Jenny. How
does it feel to be the loser of the highest-scoring match to date?"
She shakes her head. I think she's a bit upset. "You scored 358,
normally enough to win comfortably. But you were up against
the man on form. QUALITY, OVARIES, AMNIOTIC…" She's
not speaking to the banana so I turn it on myself: "Geoff, what
does this win mean? Well, it means: Scrabble's coming home, it's
coming home, it's coming home, it's coming, Scrabble's coming
home…"

Now at last she picks the board up and funnels the letters down
on my head. Little chunks of plastic confetti. It's a good feeling
and as eloquent and gracious an acknowledgement of my victory
as I know I deserve.

I put the game and the banana away, make coffee, Jenny fishes
out the *Best of Morecambe and Wise* DVD and we sit and watch
Eric and Ernie in their golden Eddie Braben BBC years. We
smile, then snicker, then slap the side of the sofa. "It doesn't get
any better than this," I say, when we're done. "I've got to go,"
she says. Off to Mr NewBloke's. I'm happy for her. Dad would
be too. "Good luck," I say she gives me a hug and a kiss. She
pats Dad's urn on the way out. "What do you think of it so far?"
she says, bravely.

When she's gone I take Dad, and a table spoon, into the garden.
Open his lid, start ladling him out, releasing him from his trophy
life. A bit here, bit there. And as I scoop and sprinkle I speak
Sylvia Dee's words taken from the Book of Common Song,
otherwise known as 101 Greatest Hits for Buskers

"Bring me sunshine, in your smile. Bring me laughter, all the while

In this world where we live, there should be more happiness

So much joy you can give, to each brand new bright tomorrow

Make me happy, through the years. Never bring me, any tears

Let your arms be as warm as the sun from up above

Bring me fun, bring me sunshine, bring me love

Amen. There you go Dad. Happy Christmas. All the best. Th-th-th-th-th- that's all folks!"

ACKNOWLEDGEMENTS

The book would not be what it is without the wonderful cover and illustrations by Claudia Schmid. I'm also grateful to Claudia for allowing me to write poems inspired by existing drawings. I hope this book leads to further collaborations.

My gratitude goes too to Frances Crow who did the layout and design for little more than the price of an Indian head massage. Thank you Frances!

Many of the poems were first written for and broadcast on Radio 4's *Saturday Live*. Warm thanks to Dixi Stewart, Maggie Olgiati, JP Devlin and the team.

Longer versions of some of the prose pieces appeared in my *Walk on the Mild Side* column in *Kindred Spirit* magazine – thanks to then-editor Richard Beaumont.

Thwok! was written in my capacity as Official Wimbledon Championships Poet in 2010, undertaken in collaboration with The Poetry Trust. Special thanks to Naomi Jaffa, Director of TPT, and to Rosabel Richards.

The Hideous Bloat was an 'extra' for the song cycle *A Little Book of Monsters* written with composer Stephen Deazley and first performed by Linda Ormiston at the St Magnus Festival, Orkney, 2012.

Deep Time and *Tilly and Cliff* are part of *Jurassic Journey,* a collaboration with photographer Ben Osborne, composer Sammy Hurden and sculptor Lal Hitchcock. Thanks too to everyone at Artsreach and Villages In Action.

Respectfully Yours is a lyric from the song cycle *The Same Flame,* written with composer Thomas Hewitt Jones, commissioned by Churchill Music!, published by Boosey and Hawkes and released by Vivum.

The adventures of *Empath Man* were broadcast on Radio 4 and wouldn't have come to the airwaves without the compassionate intervention of Mark Smalley who continues, quixotically, to champion the Skinless Wonder in his quest to become a Musical.

Some of these poems and stories have been recorded for Radio 4's *Wondermentalist Cabaret* – thanks once again to Mark Smalley, to Alison Crawford and to Jerri Hart – one-man house band, film-maker and trifle eater. (That's enough about Jerri.)

Say it with Flowers was first published in Resurgence/Ecologist magazine and originally written for the 2nd series of the *Wondermentalist Cabaret*. *Putting It Across* and *Regaining the Ashes* were commissioned by producers Peter Everett and Chris Hall respectively and first broadcast on Radio 4.

Big thanks to my wife, Heather, my sons Finn and Tom and my parents Tim and Sheila Harvey, for love, support and sounding-board skills.

Last but not least special thanks to Lynne Gerlach, without whose unfailing enthusiasm & generous encouragement this book would not have come into being – well, certainly not before Christmas.

These pages are left blank for your enjoyment

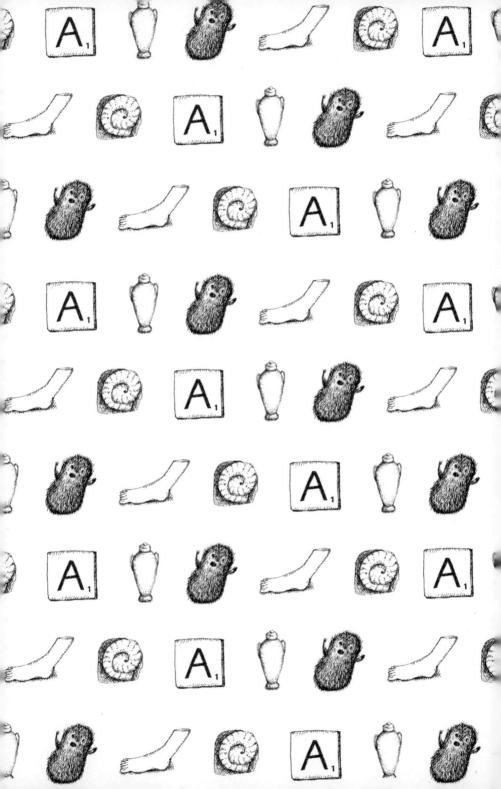